THE ULTIMATE
Social Media Planner

This Planner Belongs To:

_____

Contact Information:

 _____

 _____

 _____

THE ULTIMATE
Social
Media
Planner

Copyright Notice

Index

Content Planner Pages

Page	Title

Dimensions Cheat Sheet

Note: All sizes are measured in pixels.
Measurements are width by height.

 FACEBOOK SIZE RECOMMENDATIONS:

Profile Picture: 170 x 170
Cover Photo: 851 x 315
Square Post: 1200 x 1200
Portrait Post: 630 x 1200
Stories: 1080 x 1920
Ads: Min.1080 x 1080

 INSTAGRAM SIZE RECOMMENDATIONS:

Profile Picture: 320 x 320
Stories: 1080 x 1920
Square Post: 1080 x 1080
Portrait Post: 1080 x 1350
Landscape: 1080 x 566
Stories Ads: 1080 x 1920

 PINTEREST SIZE RECOMMENDATIONS:

Profile Picture: 165 x 165
Profile Cover: 800 x 450 min
Pins: 1000 x 1500
Story Pins: 1080 x 1920
Fleets: 1080 x 1920

 SNAPCHAT SIZE RECOMMENDATIONS:

Ads size: 1080 x 1920 min
Geofilter: 1080 x 1920 min

 TWITTER SIZE RECOMMENDATIONS:

Profile Picture: 400 x 400
Header Photo: 1500 x 500
In-Stream Photo: 1600 x 1900
Post Image: 1200 x 675
Video: 720 x 720

 LINKEDIN SIZE RECOMMENDATIONS:

Profile Picture: 400 x 400
Cover Photo: 1584 x 396
Blog Post Img: 1200 x 627
Biz Banner: 646 x 220
Biz Logo: 300 x 300
Square Post: 1200 x 1200
Portrait Post: 1080 x 1350

 TIKTOK SIZE RECOMMENDATIONS:

Profile Photo: 200 x 200
Video: 1080 x 1920
In-feed ad ratio: 9:16, 1:1, 16:9

 YOUTUBE SIZE RECOMMENDATIONS:

Profile Photo: 800 x 800
Banners: 2048 x 1152 min
Video: 1280 x 720 min
Thumbnail: 1280 x 720

All information accurate at time of list creation.

Follower Tracker

	Start	Month 1	Month 2	Month 3	Month 4	Month 5	Month 6
Date:							

Hashtag Research

Reminder: It's important to use a mix of hashtags with differing levels of competition, don't reuse the same hashtags on each post, do your research, make them unique and make them count!

High Competition Hashtags (Over 500k Posts)

\# _____   \# _____
\# _____   \# _____
\# _____   \# _____
\# _____   \# _____
\# _____   \# _____
\# _____   \# _____
\# _____   \# _____

Medium Competition Hashtags (100k-500k Posts)

\# _____   \# _____
\# _____   \# _____
\# _____   \# _____
\# _____   \# _____
\# _____   \# _____
\# _____   \# _____
\# _____   \# _____

Low Competition Hashtags (Under 100k Posts)

\# _____   \# _____
\# _____   \# _____
\# _____   \# _____
\# _____   \# _____
\# _____   \# _____
\# _____   \# _____
\# _____   \# _____

Password Info

Network: _____

Username: _____

Password: _____

E-mail: _____

Notes: _____

Network: _____

Username: _____

Password: _____

E-mail: _____

Notes: _____

Network: _____

Username: _____

Password: _____

E-mail: _____

Notes: _____

Network: _____

Username: _____

Password: _____

E-mail: _____

Notes: _____

Password Info Cont.

Network: _____

Username: _____

Password: _____

E-mail: _____

Notes: _____

Network: _____

Username: _____

Password: _____

E-mail: _____

Notes: _____

Network: _____

Username: _____

Password: _____

E-mail: _____

Notes: _____

Network: _____

Username: _____

Password: _____

E-mail: _____

Notes: _____

Additional Notes: _____

_____

Branding Basics

Aesthetic

General Feel: _____
Inspirations: _____

Logo File Location: _____

Formats: ☐ .PNG ☐ .JPG ☐ .AI ☐ .SVG ☐ .PDF

Typography:

Typeface 1: _____
Notes: _____
Typeface 2: _____
Notes: _____

Colorography

	Color 1: _____		Color 2: _____
	HEX: _____		HEX: _____
	Notes: _____		Notes: _____

Color 1: _____
HEX: _____
Notes: _____

Color 2: _____
HEX: _____
Notes: _____

Color 1: _____
HEX: _____
Notes: _____

Color 2: _____
HEX: _____
Notes: _____

Target Audience:

Age Range: _____   Gender(s): _____   Salary: _____
Hobbies: _____
Location: _____
Other: _____

Content Ideas

- Behind the Scenes Photo
- Inspirational Quote
- Sneak Peak
- Workspace Photo
- Throwback Thursday (#tbt)
- Tutorial
- Freebie
- Contest
- Product Recommendation
- Business Promotion
- Thank Audience
- Challenge Post
- Poll
- Giveaway
- Seasonal Post
- Tip of the Day
- Product Promotion
- Video Content
- FAQ of the Day
- Holiday Post
- Question for Audience
- Motivation Monday
- Contest Winner
- Blog Post Feature
- Discount/Specials
- Flashback Friday
- Personal Level Post
- Hobbies

- Fill in the Blank
- Social-Only Promo
- Weekend Plans
- Optimistic Post
- Pet Picture
- Case Study
- Industry Related Post
- Guides
- Meme / Joke Post
- Fun Fact about
- This-or-That Question
- Day-in-the-life Post
- Monthly Goals
- Review/Testimonial
- Customer Appreciation
- Raise Awareness for Issue
- Follower Spotlight
- Infographics
- Events / Life Update
- Recommendations
- Share News
- Lyrics
- Self-care Post
- Time-saving Tip
- Music You're Loving
- Favorite Tools
- Favorite Finds
- Share a Milestone

Income Tracker

Month:		
Source	Amount	Paid?

Month Total: **Year Total:**

Month:		
Source	Amount	Paid?

Month Total: **Year Total:**

Month:		
Source	Amount	Paid?

Month Total: **Year Total:**

Month:		
Source	Amount	Paid?

Month Total: **Year Total:**

Month:		
Source	Amount	Paid?

Month Total: **Year Total:**

Month:		
Source	Amount	Paid?

Month Total: **Year Total:**

Expenses Tracker

Product/Service:	Reason:	Cost:	Total:

Competitor Analysis

Competitior: _____

Account Handles: _____

Follower Count: _____

Best Networks: _____

Best Posts: _____

Notes: _____

_____

_____

Competitior: _____

Account Handles: _____

Follower Count: _____

Best Networks: _____

Best Posts: _____

Notes: _____

_____

_____

Competitior: _____

Account Handles: _____

Follower Count: _____

Best Networks: _____

Best Posts: _____

Notes: _____

_____

_____

Monthly Planner

MON	TUE	WED	THU	FRI	SAT	SUN

Events:

_____
_____
_____
_____
_____

To Do List:

☐ _____
☐ _____
☐ _____
☐ _____
☐ _____

Notes:

Weekly Planner

Most Important:

_____

_____

_____

_____

To Do List:

- ☐ _____
- ☐ _____
- ☐ _____
- ☐ _____
- ☐ _____
- ☐ _____
- ☐ _____

Goals: _____

_____

_____

Monday

Tuesday	Wednesday

Thursday	Friday

Saturday	Sunday

MONDAY

To Dos:

☐ _____
☐ _____
☐ _____
☐ _____
☐ _____
☐ _____

Notes:

_____
_____
_____
_____
_____
_____

TUESDAY

DATE: _____

To Dos:

☐ _____
☐ _____
☐ _____
☐ _____
☐ _____
☐ _____

Notes:

_____
_____
_____
_____
_____
_____

WEDNESDAY

DATE: _____

To Dos:

☐ _____
☐ _____
☐ _____
☐ _____
☐ _____
☐ _____

Notes:

_____
_____
_____
_____
_____
_____

THURSDAY

DATE: _____

To Dos:

☐ _____
☐ _____
☐ _____
☐ _____
☐ _____
☐ _____

Notes:

_____
_____
_____
_____
_____
_____

FRIDAY

To Dos:
- [ ] _____
- [ ] _____
- [ ] _____
- [ ] _____
- [ ] _____
- [ ] _____

Notes:
_____
_____
_____
_____
_____
_____
_____

SATURDAY

DATE: _____

To Dos:
- [ ] _____
- [ ] _____
- [ ] _____
- [ ] _____
- [ ] _____
- [ ] _____

Notes:
_____
_____
_____
_____
_____
_____
_____

SUNDAY

DATE: _____

To Dos:
- [ ] _____
- [ ] _____
- [ ] _____
- [ ] _____
- [ ] _____
- [ ] _____

Notes:
_____
_____
_____
_____
_____
_____
_____

WEEKLY RECAP:

Rating: ☆☆☆☆☆

BEST PERFORMING POST:
_____
_____
_____

Platform:

Posts:

14

Weekly Planner

Most Important:

_____
_____
_____
_____
_____

To Do List:

☐ _____
☐ _____
☐ _____
☐ _____
☐ _____
☐ _____
☐ _____

Monday

Goals: _____
_____
_____

Tuesday	Wednesday

Thursday	Friday

Saturday	Sunday

MONDAY

To Dos:

☐ _____
☐ _____
☐ _____
☐ _____
☐ _____
☐ _____

Notes:

_____
_____
_____
_____
_____
_____

TUESDAY

DATE: _____

To Dos:

☐ _____
☐ _____
☐ _____
☐ _____
☐ _____
☐ _____

Notes:

_____
_____
_____
_____
_____
_____

WEDNESDAY

DATE: _____

To Dos:

☐ _____
☐ _____
☐ _____
☐ _____
☐ _____
☐ _____

Notes:

_____
_____
_____
_____
_____
_____

THURSDAY

DATE: _____

To Dos:

☐ _____
☐ _____
☐ _____
☐ _____
☐ _____
☐ _____

Notes:

_____
_____
_____
_____
_____
_____

FRIDAY

To Dos:
- [ ] _____
- [ ] _____
- [ ] _____
- [ ] _____
- [ ] _____
- [ ] _____

Notes:
_____
_____
_____
_____
_____
_____

SATURDAY

DATE: _____

To Dos:
- [ ] _____
- [ ] _____
- [ ] _____
- [ ] _____
- [ ] _____
- [ ] _____

Notes:
_____
_____
_____
_____
_____
_____

SUNDAY

DATE: _____

To Dos:
- [ ] _____
- [ ] _____
- [ ] _____
- [ ] _____
- [ ] _____
- [ ] _____

Notes:
_____
_____
_____
_____
_____
_____

WEEKLY RECAP:

Rating: ☆☆☆☆☆

BEST PERFORMING POST:

_____
_____
_____

Platform:

Posts:							
[ ]	[ ]	[ ]	[ ]	[ ]	[ ]	[ ]	[ ]
[ ]	[ ]	[ ]	[ ]	[ ]	[ ]	[ ]	[ ]
[ ]	[ ]	[ ]	[ ]	[ ]	[ ]	[ ]	[ ]
[ ]	[ ]	[ ]	[ ]	[ ]	[ ]	[ ]	[ ]
[ ]	[ ]	[ ]	[ ]	[ ]	[ ]	[ ]	[ ]

Weekly Planner

Most Important:

_____
_____
_____
_____
_____

To Do List:

☐ _____
☐ _____
☐ _____
☐ _____
☐ _____
☐ _____
☐ _____

Goals: _____

_____
_____

Monday

Tuesday	Wednesday

Thursday	Friday

Saturday	Sunday

MONDAY

To Dos:

☐ _____
☐ _____
☐ _____
☐ _____
☐ _____
☐ _____

Notes:

_____
_____
_____
_____
_____
_____

TUESDAY

DATE: _____

To Dos:

☐ _____
☐ _____
☐ _____
☐ _____
☐ _____
☐ _____

Notes:

_____
_____
_____
_____
_____
_____

WEDNESDAY

DATE: _____

To Dos:

☐ _____
☐ _____
☐ _____
☐ _____
☐ _____
☐ _____

Notes:

_____
_____
_____
_____
_____
_____

THURSDAY

DATE: _____

To Dos:

☐ _____
☐ _____
☐ _____
☐ _____
☐ _____
☐ _____

Notes:

_____
_____
_____
_____
_____

FRIDAY

To Dos:
- [ ] _____
- [ ] _____
- [ ] _____
- [ ] _____
- [ ] _____
- [ ] _____

Notes:
_____
_____
_____
_____
_____
_____

SATURDAY

DATE: _____

To Dos:
- [ ] _____
- [ ] _____
- [ ] _____
- [ ] _____
- [ ] _____
- [ ] _____

Notes:
_____
_____
_____
_____
_____
_____

SUNDAY

DATE: _____

To Dos:
- [ ] _____
- [ ] _____
- [ ] _____
- [ ] _____
- [ ] _____
- [ ] _____

Notes:
_____
_____
_____
_____
_____
_____

WEEKLY RECAP:

Rating: ☆☆☆☆☆

BEST PERFORMING POST:

_____
_____
_____

Platform:

🐦	👻	f	in	♪	📷	▶	📌
Posts:							
☐	☐	☐	☐	☐	☐	☐	☐
☐	☐	☐	☐	☐	☐	☐	☐
☐	☐	☐	☐	☐	☐	☐	☐
☐	☐	☐	☐	☐	☐	☐	☐
☐	☐	☐	☐	☐	☐	☐	☐

Weekly Planner

Most Important:

_____
_____
_____
_____

To Do List:

- ☐ _____
- ☐ _____
- ☐ _____
- ☐ _____
- ☐ _____
- ☐ _____
- ☐ _____

Goals: _____

_____
_____

Monday

Tuesday

Wednesday

Thursday

Friday

Saturday

Sunday

MONDAY

To Dos:

☐ _____
☐ _____
☐ _____
☐ _____
☐ _____
☐ _____

Notes:

_____
_____
_____
_____
_____
_____

TUESDAY

DATE: _____

To Dos:

☐ _____
☐ _____
☐ _____
☐ _____
☐ _____
☐ _____

Notes:

_____
_____
_____
_____
_____
_____

WEDNESDAY

DATE: _____

To Dos:

☐ _____
☐ _____
☐ _____
☐ _____
☐ _____
☐ _____

Notes:

_____
_____
_____
_____
_____
_____

THURSDAY

DATE: _____

To Dos:

☐ _____
☐ _____
☐ _____
☐ _____
☐ _____
☐ _____

Notes:

_____
_____
_____
_____
_____
_____

FRIDAY

To Dos:
- ☐ _____
- ☐ _____
- ☐ _____
- ☐ _____
- ☐ _____
- ☐ _____

DATE: _____ WEEK: _____

Notes:
_____
_____
_____
_____
_____
_____

SATURDAY

To Dos:
- ☐ _____
- ☐ _____
- ☐ _____
- ☐ _____
- ☐ _____
- ☐ _____

DATE: _____

Notes:
_____
_____
_____
_____
_____
_____

SUNDAY

To Dos:
- ☐ _____
- ☐ _____
- ☐ _____
- ☐ _____
- ☐ _____
- ☐ _____

DATE: _____

Notes:
_____
_____
_____
_____
_____
_____

WEEKLY RECAP: **Platform:**

Rating: ☆☆☆☆☆ **Posts:**

BEST PERFORMING POST:

_____
_____
_____

Weekly Planner

Most Important:

_____
_____
_____
_____
_____

To Do List:

☐ _____
☐ _____
☐ _____
☐ _____
☐ _____
☐ _____
☐ _____

Goals: _____

_____
_____

Monday

Tuesday	Wednesday

Thursday	Friday

Saturday	Sunday

MONDAY

To Dos:

☐ _____

☐ _____

☐ _____

☐ _____

☐ _____

☐ _____

Notes:

_____

_____

_____

_____

_____

_____

TUESDAY

DATE: _____

To Dos:

☐ _____

☐ _____

☐ _____

☐ _____

☐ _____

☐ _____

Notes:

_____

_____

_____

_____

_____

_____

WEDNESDAY

DATE: _____

To Dos:

☐ _____

☐ _____

☐ _____

☐ _____

☐ _____

☐ _____

Notes:

_____

_____

_____

_____

_____

_____

THURSDAY

DATE: _____

To Dos:

☐ _____

☐ _____

☐ _____

☐ _____

☐ _____

☐ _____

Notes:

_____

_____

_____

_____

_____

_____

FRIDAY

DATE: _____ WEEK: _____

To Dos:

- [ ] _____
- [ ] _____
- [ ] _____
- [ ] _____
- [ ] _____
- [ ] _____

Notes:

_____
_____
_____
_____
_____
_____

SATURDAY

DATE: _____

To Dos:

- [ ] _____
- [ ] _____
- [ ] _____
- [ ] _____
- [ ] _____
- [ ] _____

Notes:

_____
_____
_____
_____
_____
_____

SUNDAY

DATE: _____

To Dos:

- [ ] _____
- [ ] _____
- [ ] _____
- [ ] _____
- [ ] _____
- [ ] _____

Notes:

_____
_____
_____
_____
_____
_____

WEEKLY RECAP:

Rating: ☆☆☆☆☆

BEST PERFORMING POST:

_____
_____

Platform:

🐦	👻	f	in	♪	📷	▶	📌
Posts:							
☐	☐	☐	☐	☐	☐	☐	☐
☐	☐	☐	☐	☐	☐	☐	☐
☐	☐	☐	☐	☐	☐	☐	☐
☐	☐	☐	☐	☐	☐	☐	☐
☐	☐	☐	☐	☐	☐	☐	☐

Monthly Planner

MON	TUE	WED	THU	FRI	SAT	SUN

Events:

To Do List:

☐ _____
☐ _____
☐ _____
☐ _____
☐ _____

Notes:

27

Weekly Planner

Most Important:

_____
_____
_____
_____

To Do List:

☐ _____
☐ _____
☐ _____
☐ _____
☐ _____
☐ _____
☐ _____

Goals: _____

_____
_____

Monday

Tuesday	Wednesday

Thursday	Friday

Saturday	Sunday

MONDAY

To Dos:

☐ _____
☐ _____
☐ _____
☐ _____
☐ _____
☐ _____

Notes:

_____
_____
_____
_____
_____
_____
_____

TUESDAY

DATE: _____

To Dos:

☐ _____
☐ _____
☐ _____
☐ _____
☐ _____
☐ _____

Notes:

_____
_____
_____
_____
_____
_____
_____

WEDNESDAY

DATE: _____

To Dos:

☐ _____
☐ _____
☐ _____
☐ _____
☐ _____
☐ _____

Notes:

_____
_____
_____
_____
_____
_____
_____

THURSDAY

DATE: _____

To Dos:

☐ _____
☐ _____
☐ _____
☐ _____
☐ _____
☐ _____

Notes:

_____
_____
_____
_____
_____
_____

FRIDAY

DATE: _____ WEEK: _____

To Dos:

- [ ] _____
- [ ] _____
- [ ] _____
- [ ] _____
- [ ] _____
- [ ] _____

Notes:

_____
_____
_____
_____
_____
_____

SATURDAY

DATE: _____

To Dos:

- [ ] _____
- [ ] _____
- [ ] _____
- [ ] _____
- [ ] _____
- [ ] _____

Notes:

_____
_____
_____
_____
_____
_____

SUNDAY

DATE: _____

To Dos:

- [ ] _____
- [ ] _____
- [ ] _____
- [ ] _____
- [ ] _____
- [ ] _____

Notes:

_____
_____
_____
_____
_____
_____

WEEKLY RECAP:

Rating: ☆☆☆☆☆

BEST PERFORMING POST:

_____
_____
_____

Platform: 🐦 👻 f in ♪ 📷 ▶ 𝓟

Posts:

🐦	👻	f	in	♪	📷	▶	𝓟
☐	☐	☐	☐	☐	☐	☐	☐
☐	☐	☐	☐	☐	☐	☐	☐
☐	☐	☐	☐	☐	☐	☐	☐
☐	☐	☐	☐	☐	☐	☐	☐
☐	☐	☐	☐	☐	☐	☐	☐

Weekly Planner

Most Important:

_____
_____
_____
_____
_____

To Do List:

- ☐ _____
- ☐ _____
- ☐ _____
- ☐ _____
- ☐ _____
- ☐ _____
- ☐ _____

Goals: _____

_____
_____

Monday

Tuesday	Wednesday

Thursday	Friday

Saturday	Sunday

MONDAY

To Dos:

☐ _____
☐ _____
☐ _____
☐ _____
☐ _____
☐ _____

Notes:

_____
_____
_____
_____
_____
_____

TUESDAY

DATE: _____

To Dos:

☐ _____
☐ _____
☐ _____
☐ _____
☐ _____
☐ _____

Notes:

_____
_____
_____
_____
_____
_____

WEDNESDAY

DATE: _____

To Dos:

☐ _____
☐ _____
☐ _____
☐ _____
☐ _____
☐ _____

Notes:

_____
_____
_____
_____
_____
_____

THURSDAY

DATE: _____

To Dos:

☐ _____
☐ _____
☐ _____
☐ _____
☐ _____
☐ _____

Notes:

_____
_____
_____
_____
_____
_____

FRIDAY

To Dos:
- [ ] _____
- [ ] _____
- [ ] _____
- [ ] _____
- [ ] _____
- [ ] _____

Notes:
_____
_____
_____
_____
_____
_____

SATURDAY

DATE: _____

To Dos:
- [ ] _____
- [ ] _____
- [ ] _____
- [ ] _____
- [ ] _____
- [ ] _____

Notes:
_____
_____
_____
_____
_____
_____

SUNDAY

DATE: _____

To Dos:
- [ ] _____
- [ ] _____
- [ ] _____
- [ ] _____
- [ ] _____
- [ ] _____

Notes:
_____
_____
_____
_____
_____
_____

WEEKLY RECAP: **Platform:**

Rating: ☆☆☆☆☆   **Posts:**

BEST PERFORMING POST:

_____
_____
_____

Weekly Planner

Most Important:

_____
_____
_____
_____

To Do List:

☐ _____
☐ _____
☐ _____
☐ _____
☐ _____
☐ _____
☐ _____

Goals: _____

_____
_____

Monday

Tuesday	Wednesday

Thursday	Friday

Saturday	Sunday

MONDAY

To Dos:

☐ _____
☐ _____
☐ _____
☐ _____
☐ _____
☐ _____

Notes:

_____
_____
_____
_____
_____
_____

TUESDAY

DATE: _____

To Dos:

☐ _____
☐ _____
☐ _____
☐ _____
☐ _____
☐ _____

Notes:

_____
_____
_____
_____
_____
_____

WEDNESDAY

DATE: _____

To Dos:

☐ _____
☐ _____
☐ _____
☐ _____
☐ _____
☐ _____

Notes:

_____
_____
_____
_____
_____
_____

THURSDAY

DATE: _____

To Dos:

☐ _____
☐ _____
☐ _____
☐ _____
☐ _____
☐ _____

Notes:

_____
_____
_____
_____
_____
_____

FRIDAY

To Dos:

- ☐ _____
- ☐ _____
- ☐ _____
- ☐ _____
- ☐ _____
- ☐ _____

Notes:

_____
_____
_____
_____
_____
_____

SATURDAY

DATE: _____

To Dos:

- ☐ _____
- ☐ _____
- ☐ _____
- ☐ _____
- ☐ _____
- ☐ _____

Notes:

_____
_____
_____
_____
_____
_____

SUNDAY

DATE: _____

To Dos:

- ☐ _____
- ☐ _____
- ☐ _____
- ☐ _____
- ☐ _____
- ☐ _____

Notes:

_____
_____
_____
_____
_____
_____

WEEKLY RECAP:

Rating: ☆☆☆☆☆

BEST PERFORMING POST:

_____
_____
_____

Platform: 🐦 👻 f in ♪ 📷 ▶ 📌

Posts:

☐	☐	☐	☐	☐	☐	☐	☐
☐	☐	☐	☐	☐	☐	☐	☐
☐	☐	☐	☐	☐	☐	☐	☐
☐	☐	☐	☐	☐	☐	☐	☐
☐	☐	☐	☐	☐	☐	☐	☐

Weekly Planner

Most Important:

_____

_____

_____

_____

To Do List:

☐ _____

☐ _____

☐ _____

☐ _____

☐ _____

☐ _____

☐ _____

Goals: _____

_____

_____

Monday

Tuesday	Wednesday

Thursday	Friday

Saturday	Sunday

MONDAY

DATE: _____ WEEK: _____

To Dos:

☐ _____

☐ _____

☐ _____

☐ _____

☐ _____

☐ _____

Notes:

_____

_____

_____

_____

_____

_____

TUESDAY

DATE: _____

To Dos:

☐ _____

☐ _____

☐ _____

☐ _____

☐ _____

☐ _____

Notes:

_____

_____

_____

_____

_____

_____

WEDNESDAY

DATE: _____

To Dos:

☐ _____

☐ _____

☐ _____

☐ _____

☐ _____

☐ _____

Notes:

_____

_____

_____

_____

_____

_____

THURSDAY

DATE: _____

To Dos:

☐ _____

☐ _____

☐ _____

☐ _____

☐ _____

☐ _____

Notes:

_____

_____

_____

_____

_____

_____

FRIDAY

To Dos:
- [ ] _____
- [ ] _____
- [ ] _____
- [ ] _____
- [ ] _____
- [ ] _____

Notes:
_____
_____
_____
_____
_____
_____

SATURDAY

DATE: _____

To Dos:
- [ ] _____
- [ ] _____
- [ ] _____
- [ ] _____
- [ ] _____
- [ ] _____

Notes:
_____
_____
_____
_____
_____
_____

SUNDAY

DATE: _____

To Dos:
- [ ] _____
- [ ] _____
- [ ] _____
- [ ] _____
- [ ] _____
- [ ] _____

Notes:
_____
_____
_____
_____
_____
_____

WEEKLY RECAP: **Platform:** 🐦 👻 f in ♪ 📷 ▶ 📌

Rating: ☆☆☆☆☆ **Posts:**

BEST PERFORMING POST:

_____
_____
_____

Weekly Planner

Most Important:

_____
_____
_____
_____

To Do List:

☐ _____
☐ _____
☐ _____
☐ _____
☐ _____
☐ _____
☐ _____

Goals: _____

_____
_____

Monday

Tuesday	Wednesday

Thursday	Friday

Saturday	Sunday

MONDAY

To Dos:

- ☐ _____
- ☐ _____
- ☐ _____
- ☐ _____
- ☐ _____
- ☐ _____

DATE: _____ WEEK: _____

Notes:

_____
_____
_____
_____
_____
_____

TUESDAY

To Dos:

- ☐ _____
- ☐ _____
- ☐ _____
- ☐ _____
- ☐ _____
- ☐ _____

DATE: _____

Notes:

_____
_____
_____
_____
_____
_____

WEDNESDAY

To Dos:

- ☐ _____
- ☐ _____
- ☐ _____
- ☐ _____
- ☐ _____
- ☐ _____

DATE: _____

Notes:

_____
_____
_____
_____
_____
_____

THURSDAY

To Dos:

- ☐ _____
- ☐ _____
- ☐ _____
- ☐ _____
- ☐ _____
- ☐ _____

DATE: _____

Notes:

_____
_____
_____
_____
_____
_____

FRIDAY

To Dos:
- ☐ _____
- ☐ _____
- ☐ _____
- ☐ _____
- ☐ _____
- ☐ _____

Notes:
_____
_____
_____
_____
_____
_____
_____

SATURDAY

DATE: _____

To Dos:
- ☐ _____
- ☐ _____
- ☐ _____
- ☐ _____
- ☐ _____
- ☐ _____

Notes:
_____
_____
_____
_____
_____
_____
_____

SUNDAY

DATE: _____

To Dos:
- ☐ _____
- ☐ _____
- ☐ _____
- ☐ _____
- ☐ _____
- ☐ _____

Notes:
_____
_____
_____
_____
_____
_____
_____

WEEKLY RECAP:

Rating: ☆☆☆☆☆

BEST PERFORMING POST:
_____
_____
_____

Platform: 🐦 👻 f in ♪ 📷 ▶ 𝒫

Posts:

🐦	👻	f	in	♪	📷	▶	𝒫
☐	☐	☐	☐	☐	☐	☐	☐
☐	☐	☐	☐	☐	☐	☐	☐
☐	☐	☐	☐	☐	☐	☐	☐
☐	☐	☐	☐	☐	☐	☐	☐
☐	☐	☐	☐	☐	☐	☐	☐

Monthly Planner

MON	TUE	WED	THU	FRI	SAT	SUN

Events:

_____

_____

_____

_____

_____

To Do List:

☐ _____

☐ _____

☐ _____

☐ _____

☐ _____

Notes:

Weekly Planner

Most Important:

_____
_____
_____
_____

To Do List:

☐ _____
☐ _____
☐ _____
☐ _____
☐ _____
☐ _____
☐ _____

Monday

Goals: _____

_____
_____

Tuesday

Wednesday

Thursday

Friday

Saturday

Sunday

MONDAY

DATE: _____ WEEK: _____

To Dos:

☐ _____
☐ _____
☐ _____
☐ _____
☐ _____
☐ _____

Notes:

_____
_____
_____
_____
_____
_____

TUESDAY

DATE: _____

To Dos:

☐ _____
☐ _____
☐ _____
☐ _____
☐ _____
☐ _____

Notes:

_____
_____
_____
_____
_____
_____

WEDNESDAY

DATE: _____

To Dos:

☐ _____
☐ _____
☐ _____
☐ _____
☐ _____
☐ _____

Notes:

_____
_____
_____
_____
_____
_____

THURSDAY

DATE: _____

To Dos:

☐ _____
☐ _____
☐ _____
☐ _____
☐ _____
☐ _____

Notes:

_____
_____
_____
_____
_____
_____

FRIDAY

To Dos:

- ☐ _____
- ☐ _____
- ☐ _____
- ☐ _____
- ☐ _____
- ☐ _____

Notes:

_____
_____
_____
_____
_____
_____

SATURDAY

DATE: _____

To Dos:

- ☐ _____
- ☐ _____
- ☐ _____
- ☐ _____
- ☐ _____
- ☐ _____

Notes:

_____
_____
_____
_____
_____
_____

SUNDAY

DATE: _____

To Dos:

- ☐ _____
- ☐ _____
- ☐ _____
- ☐ _____
- ☐ _____
- ☐ _____

Notes:

_____
_____
_____
_____
_____
_____

WEEKLY RECAP:

Rating: ☆☆☆☆☆

BEST PERFORMING POST:

_____
_____
_____

Platform: 🐦 👻 f in ♪ 📷 ▶ 𝓟

Posts:

🐦	👻	f	in	♪	📷	▶	𝓟
☐	☐	☐	☐	☐	☐	☐	☐
☐	☐	☐	☐	☐	☐	☐	☐
☐	☐	☐	☐	☐	☐	☐	☐
☐	☐	☐	☐	☐	☐	☐	☐
☐	☐	☐	☐	☐	☐	☐	☐

Weekly Planner

Most Important:

To Do List:

☐ _____
☐ _____
☐ _____
☐ _____
☐ _____
☐ _____
☐ _____

Monday

Goals: _____

Tuesday	Wednesday

Thursday	Friday

Saturday	Sunday

MONDAY

DATE: _____ WEEK: _____

To Dos:

☐ _____
☐ _____
☐ _____
☐ _____
☐ _____
☐ _____

Notes:

_____
_____
_____
_____
_____
_____

TUESDAY

DATE: _____

To Dos:

☐ _____
☐ _____
☐ _____
☐ _____
☐ _____
☐ _____

Notes:

_____
_____
_____
_____
_____
_____

WEDNESDAY

DATE: _____

To Dos:

☐ _____
☐ _____
☐ _____
☐ _____
☐ _____
☐ _____

Notes:

_____
_____
_____
_____
_____
_____

THURSDAY

DATE: _____

To Dos:

☐ _____
☐ _____
☐ _____
☐ _____
☐ _____
☐ _____

Notes:

_____
_____
_____
_____
_____
_____

FRIDAY

To Dos:
- ☐ _____
- ☐ _____
- ☐ _____
- ☐ _____
- ☐ _____
- ☐ _____

Notes:
_____
_____
_____
_____
_____
_____

SATURDAY

DATE: _____

To Dos:
- ☐ _____
- ☐ _____
- ☐ _____
- ☐ _____
- ☐ _____
- ☐ _____

Notes:
_____
_____
_____
_____
_____
_____

SUNDAY

DATE: _____

To Dos:
- ☐ _____
- ☐ _____
- ☐ _____
- ☐ _____
- ☐ _____
- ☐ _____

Notes:
_____
_____
_____
_____
_____
_____

WEEKLY RECAP: **Platform:**

Rating: ☆☆☆☆☆   **Posts:**

BEST PERFORMING POST:

_____
_____
_____

Weekly Planner

Most Important:

_____
_____
_____
_____

To Do List:

☐ _____
☐ _____
☐ _____
☐ _____
☐ _____
☐ _____
☐ _____

Goals: _____
_____
_____

Monday

Tuesday	Wednesday

Thursday	Friday

Saturday	Sunday

MONDAY

To Dos:

☐ _____
☐ _____
☐ _____
☐ _____
☐ _____
☐ _____

DATE: _____ **WEEK:** _____

Notes:

_____
_____
_____
_____
_____
_____
_____

TUESDAY

To Dos:

☐ _____
☐ _____
☐ _____
☐ _____
☐ _____
☐ _____

DATE: _____

Notes:

_____
_____
_____
_____
_____
_____

WEDNESDAY

To Dos:

☐ _____
☐ _____
☐ _____
☐ _____
☐ _____
☐ _____

DATE: _____

Notes:

_____
_____
_____
_____
_____
_____

THURSDAY

To Dos:

☐ _____
☐ _____
☐ _____
☐ _____
☐ _____
☐ _____

DATE: _____

Notes:

_____
_____
_____
_____
_____
_____

FRIDAY

DATE: _____ WEEK: _____

To Dos:
- [ ] _____
- [ ] _____
- [ ] _____
- [ ] _____
- [ ] _____
- [ ] _____

Notes:
_____
_____
_____
_____
_____
_____
_____

SATURDAY

DATE: _____

To Dos:
- [ ] _____
- [ ] _____
- [ ] _____
- [ ] _____
- [ ] _____
- [ ] _____

Notes:
_____
_____
_____
_____
_____
_____
_____

SUNDAY

DATE: _____

To Dos:
- [ ] _____
- [ ] _____
- [ ] _____
- [ ] _____
- [ ] _____
- [ ] _____

Notes:
_____
_____
_____
_____
_____
_____
_____

WEEKLY RECAP:

Rating: ☆☆☆☆☆

BEST PERFORMING POST:

_____
_____
_____

Platform:

✗	✗	f	in	♪	◉	▶	P
Posts:							
[ ]	[ ]	[ ]	[ ]	[ ]	[ ]	[ ]	[ ]
[ ]	[ ]	[ ]	[ ]	[ ]	[ ]	[ ]	[ ]
[ ]	[ ]	[ ]	[ ]	[ ]	[ ]	[ ]	[ ]
[ ]	[ ]	[ ]	[ ]	[ ]	[ ]	[ ]	[ ]
[ ]	[ ]	[ ]	[ ]	[ ]	[ ]	[ ]	[ ]

Weekly Planner

Most Important:
_____
_____
_____
_____
_____

To Do List:
- ☐ _____
- ☐ _____
- ☐ _____
- ☐ _____
- ☐ _____
- ☐ _____
- ☐ _____

Monday

Goals: _____
_____
_____

Tuesday

Wednesday

Thursday

Friday

Saturday

Sunday

MONDAY

To Dos:

☐ _____
☐ _____
☐ _____
☐ _____
☐ _____
☐ _____

Notes:

_____
_____
_____
_____
_____
_____
_____

TUESDAY

DATE: _____

To Dos:

☐ _____
☐ _____
☐ _____
☐ _____
☐ _____
☐ _____

Notes:

_____
_____
_____
_____
_____
_____
_____

WEDNESDAY

DATE: _____

To Dos:

☐ _____
☐ _____
☐ _____
☐ _____
☐ _____
☐ _____

Notes:

_____
_____
_____
_____
_____
_____
_____

THURSDAY

DATE: _____

To Dos:

☐ _____
☐ _____
☐ _____
☐ _____
☐ _____
☐ _____

Notes:

_____
_____
_____
_____
_____
_____

FRIDAY

To Dos:

- [ ] _____
- [ ] _____
- [ ] _____
- [ ] _____
- [ ] _____
- [ ] _____

Notes:

_____
_____
_____
_____
_____
_____

SATURDAY

DATE: _____

To Dos:

- [ ] _____
- [ ] _____
- [ ] _____
- [ ] _____
- [ ] _____
- [ ] _____

Notes:

_____
_____
_____
_____
_____
_____

SUNDAY

DATE: _____

To Dos:

- [ ] _____
- [ ] _____
- [ ] _____
- [ ] _____
- [ ] _____
- [ ] _____

Notes:

_____
_____
_____
_____
_____
_____

WEEKLY RECAP: **Platform:**

Rating: ☆☆☆☆☆   **Posts:**

BEST PERFORMING POST:

_____
_____
_____

Weekly Planner

Most Important:

_____
_____
_____
_____

To Do List:

☐ _____
☐ _____
☐ _____
☐ _____
☐ _____
☐ _____
☐ _____

Goals: _____
_____
_____

Monday

Tuesday

Wednesday

Thursday

Friday

Saturday

Sunday

MONDAY

To Dos:
- ☐ _____
- ☐ _____
- ☐ _____
- ☐ _____
- ☐ _____
- ☐ _____

Notes:
_____
_____
_____
_____
_____
_____

TUESDAY

DATE: _____

To Dos:
- ☐ _____
- ☐ _____
- ☐ _____
- ☐ _____
- ☐ _____
- ☐ _____

Notes:
_____
_____
_____
_____
_____
_____

WEDNESDAY

DATE: _____

To Dos:
- ☐ _____
- ☐ _____
- ☐ _____
- ☐ _____
- ☐ _____
- ☐ _____

Notes:
_____
_____
_____
_____
_____
_____

THURSDAY

DATE: _____

To Dos:
- ☐ _____
- ☐ _____
- ☐ _____
- ☐ _____
- ☐ _____
- ☐ _____

Notes:
_____
_____
_____
_____
_____
_____

FRIDAY

DATE: _____ WEEK: _____

To Dos:

- ☐ _____
- ☐ _____
- ☐ _____
- ☐ _____
- ☐ _____
- ☐ _____

Notes:

_____
_____
_____
_____
_____
_____
_____

SATURDAY

DATE: _____

To Dos:

- ☐ _____
- ☐ _____
- ☐ _____
- ☐ _____
- ☐ _____
- ☐ _____

Notes:

_____
_____
_____
_____
_____
_____
_____

SUNDAY

DATE: _____

To Dos:

- ☐ _____
- ☐ _____
- ☐ _____
- ☐ _____
- ☐ _____
- ☐ _____

Notes:

_____
_____
_____
_____
_____
_____
_____

WEEKLY RECAP: **Platform:**

Rating: ☆☆☆☆☆   **Posts:**

BEST PERFORMING POST:

_____
_____
_____

Monthly Planner

MON	TUE	WED	THU	FRI	SAT	SUN

Events:

_____

_____

_____

_____

_____

_____

To Do List:

☐ _____

☐ _____

☐ _____

☐ _____

☐ _____

Notes:

Weekly Planner

Most Important:

_____
_____
_____
_____
_____

To Do List:

☐ _____
☐ _____
☐ _____
☐ _____
☐ _____
☐ _____
☐ _____

Goals: _____
_____
_____

Monday

Tuesday	Wednesday

Thursday	Friday

Saturday	Sunday

MONDAY

To Dos:

☐ _____
☐ _____
☐ _____
☐ _____
☐ _____
☐ _____

Notes:

_____
_____
_____
_____
_____
_____

TUESDAY

DATE: _____

To Dos:

☐ _____
☐ _____
☐ _____
☐ _____
☐ _____
☐ _____

Notes:

_____
_____
_____
_____
_____
_____

WEDNESDAY

DATE: _____

To Dos:

☐ _____
☐ _____
☐ _____
☐ _____
☐ _____
☐ _____

Notes:

_____
_____
_____
_____
_____
_____

THURSDAY

DATE: _____

To Dos:

☐ _____
☐ _____
☐ _____
☐ _____
☐ _____
☐ _____

Notes:

_____
_____
_____
_____
_____
_____

FRIDAY

DATE: _____ WEEK: _____

To Dos:

☐ _____
☐ _____
☐ _____
☐ _____
☐ _____
☐ _____

Notes:

_____
_____
_____
_____
_____
_____

SATURDAY

DATE: _____

To Dos:

☐ _____
☐ _____
☐ _____
☐ _____
☐ _____
☐ _____

Notes:

_____
_____
_____
_____
_____
_____

SUNDAY

DATE: _____

To Dos:

☐ _____
☐ _____
☐ _____
☐ _____
☐ _____
☐ _____

Notes:

_____
_____
_____
_____
_____
_____

WEEKLY RECAP:

Rating: ☆☆☆☆☆

BEST PERFORMING POST:

_____
_____
_____

Platform:

Twitter	Snapchat	Facebook	LinkedIn	TikTok	Instagram	YouTube	Pinterest
☐	☐	☐	☐	☐	☐	☐	☐
☐	☐	☐	☐	☐	☐	☐	☐
☐	☐	☐	☐	☐	☐	☐	☐
☐	☐	☐	☐	☐	☐	☐	☐
☐	☐	☐	☐	☐	☐	☐	☐

Posts:

Weekly Planner

Most Important:

_____
_____
_____
_____
_____

To Do List:

☐ _____
☐ _____
☐ _____
☐ _____
☐ _____
☐ _____
☐ _____

Goals: _____
_____
_____

Monday

Tuesday	Wednesday

Thursday	Friday

Saturday	Sunday

MONDAY

To Dos:

☐ _____
☐ _____
☐ _____
☐ _____
☐ _____
☐ _____

Notes:

_____
_____
_____
_____
_____
_____
_____

TUESDAY

DATE: _____

To Dos:

☐ _____
☐ _____
☐ _____
☐ _____
☐ _____
☐ _____

Notes:

_____
_____
_____
_____
_____
_____
_____

WEDNESDAY

DATE: _____

To Dos:

☐ _____
☐ _____
☐ _____
☐ _____
☐ _____
☐ _____

Notes:

_____
_____
_____
_____
_____
_____
_____

THURSDAY

DATE: _____

To Dos:

☐ _____
☐ _____
☐ _____
☐ _____
☐ _____
☐ _____

Notes:

_____
_____
_____
_____
_____
_____
_____

FRIDAY

To Dos:
- [ ] _____
- [ ] _____
- [ ] _____
- [ ] _____
- [ ] _____
- [ ] _____

Notes:
_____
_____
_____
_____
_____

SATURDAY

DATE: _____

To Dos:
- [ ] _____
- [ ] _____
- [ ] _____
- [ ] _____
- [ ] _____
- [ ] _____

Notes:
_____
_____
_____
_____
_____
_____

SUNDAY

DATE: _____

To Dos:
- [ ] _____
- [ ] _____
- [ ] _____
- [ ] _____
- [ ] _____
- [ ] _____

Notes:
_____
_____
_____
_____
_____
_____

WEEKLY RECAP:

Rating: ☆☆☆☆☆

BEST PERFORMING POST:
_____
_____
_____

Platform:

🐦	👻	f	in	♪	📷	▶	P
Posts:							
☐	☐	☐	☐	☐	☐	☐	☐
☐	☐	☐	☐	☐	☐	☐	☐
☐	☐	☐	☐	☐	☐	☐	☐
☐	☐	☐	☐	☐	☐	☐	☐
☐	☐	☐	☐	☐	☐	☐	☐

Weekly Planner

Most Important:

_____
_____
_____
_____
_____

To Do List:

- ☐ _____
- ☐ _____
- ☐ _____
- ☐ _____
- ☐ _____
- ☐ _____
- ☐ _____

Goals: _____

_____
_____

Monday

Tuesday

Wednesday

Thursday

Friday

Saturday

Sunday

MONDAY

DATE: _____ WEEK: _____

To Dos:

☐ _____
☐ _____
☐ _____
☐ _____
☐ _____
☐ _____

Notes:

_____
_____
_____
_____
_____
_____

TUESDAY

DATE: _____

To Dos:

☐ _____
☐ _____
☐ _____
☐ _____
☐ _____
☐ _____

Notes:

_____
_____
_____
_____
_____
_____

WEDNESDAY

DATE: _____

To Dos:

☐ _____
☐ _____
☐ _____
☐ _____
☐ _____
☐ _____

Notes:

_____
_____
_____
_____
_____
_____

THURSDAY

DATE: _____

To Dos:

☐ _____
☐ _____
☐ _____
☐ _____
☐ _____
☐ _____

Notes:

_____
_____
_____
_____
_____
_____

FRIDAY

DATE: _____ WEEK: _____

To Dos:
- [ ] _____
- [ ] _____
- [ ] _____
- [ ] _____
- [ ] _____
- [ ] _____

Notes:
_____
_____
_____
_____
_____
_____

SATURDAY

DATE: _____

To Dos:
- [ ] _____
- [ ] _____
- [ ] _____
- [ ] _____
- [ ] _____
- [ ] _____

Notes:
_____
_____
_____
_____
_____
_____

SUNDAY

DATE: _____

To Dos:
- [ ] _____
- [ ] _____
- [ ] _____
- [ ] _____
- [ ] _____
- [ ] _____

Notes:
_____
_____
_____
_____
_____
_____

WEEKLY RECAP:

Rating: ☆☆☆☆☆

BEST PERFORMING POST:
_____
_____
_____

Platform: Twitter | Snapchat | Facebook | LinkedIn | TikTok | Instagram | YouTube | Pinterest

Posts:

Twitter	Snapchat	Facebook	LinkedIn	TikTok	Instagram	YouTube	Pinterest
☐	☐	☐	☐	☐	☐	☐	☐
☐	☐	☐	☐	☐	☐	☐	☐
☐	☐	☐	☐	☐	☐	☐	☐
☐	☐	☐	☐	☐	☐	☐	☐
☐	☐	☐	☐	☐	☐	☐	☐

Weekly Planner

Most Important:

_____
_____
_____
_____

To Do List:

☐ _____
☐ _____
☐ _____
☐ _____
☐ _____
☐ _____
☐ _____

Goals: _____
_____
_____

Monday

Tuesday

Wednesday

Thursday

Friday

Saturday

Sunday

MONDAY

To Dos:

- [ ] _____
- [ ] _____
- [ ] _____
- [ ] _____
- [ ] _____
- [ ] _____

Notes:

_____
_____
_____
_____
_____
_____
_____

TUESDAY

DATE: _____

To Dos:

- [ ] _____
- [ ] _____
- [ ] _____
- [ ] _____
- [ ] _____
- [ ] _____

Notes:

_____
_____
_____
_____
_____
_____
_____

WEDNESDAY

DATE: _____

To Dos:

- [ ] _____
- [ ] _____
- [ ] _____
- [ ] _____
- [ ] _____
- [ ] _____

Notes:

_____
_____
_____
_____
_____
_____
_____

THURSDAY

DATE: _____

To Dos:

- [ ] _____
- [ ] _____
- [ ] _____
- [ ] _____
- [ ] _____
- [ ] _____

Notes:

_____
_____
_____
_____
_____
_____

FRIDAY

DATE: _____ WEEK: _____

To Dos:

☐ _____

☐ _____

☐ _____

☐ _____

☐ _____

☐ _____

Notes:

_____

_____

_____

_____

_____

_____

SATURDAY

DATE: _____

To Dos:

☐ _____

☐ _____

☐ _____

☐ _____

☐ _____

☐ _____

Notes:

_____

_____

_____

_____

_____

_____

SUNDAY

DATE: _____

To Dos:

☐ _____

☐ _____

☐ _____

☐ _____

☐ _____

☐ _____

Notes:

_____

_____

_____

_____

_____

_____

WEEKLY RECAP: **Platform:**

Rating: ☆☆☆☆☆ **Posts:**

BEST PERFORMING POST:

_____

_____

_____

Weekly Planner

Most Important:

To Do List:

☐ _____
☐ _____
☐ _____
☐ _____
☐ _____
☐ _____
☐ _____

Goals: _____

Monday

Tuesday	Wednesday

Thursday	Friday

Saturday	Sunday

72

MONDAY

To Dos:

DATE: _____ WEEK: _____

Notes:

TUESDAY

To Dos:

DATE: _____

Notes:

WEDNESDAY

To Dos:

DATE: _____

Notes:

THURSDAY

To Dos:

DATE: _____

Notes:

FRIDAY

DATE: _____ WEEK: _____

To Dos:

- [ ] _____
- [ ] _____
- [ ] _____
- [ ] _____
- [ ] _____
- [ ] _____

Notes:

_____
_____
_____
_____
_____
_____

SATURDAY

DATE: _____

To Dos:

- [ ] _____
- [ ] _____
- [ ] _____
- [ ] _____
- [ ] _____
- [ ] _____

Notes:

_____
_____
_____
_____
_____
_____

SUNDAY

DATE: _____

To Dos:

- [ ] _____
- [ ] _____
- [ ] _____
- [ ] _____
- [ ] _____
- [ ] _____

Notes:

_____
_____
_____
_____
_____
_____

WEEKLY RECAP:

Rating: ☆☆☆☆☆

BEST PERFORMING POST:

_____
_____
_____

Platform: 🐦 👻 f in ♪ 📷 ▶ ⓟ

Posts:

🐦	👻	f	in	♪	📷	▶	ⓟ
☐	☐	☐	☐	☐	☐	☐	☐
☐	☐	☐	☐	☐	☐	☐	☐
☐	☐	☐	☐	☐	☐	☐	☐
☐	☐	☐	☐	☐	☐	☐	☐
☐	☐	☐	☐	☐	☐	☐	☐

Monthly Planner

MON	TUE	WED	THU	FRI	SAT	SUN

Events:

_____

_____

_____

_____

_____

To Do List:

☐ _____

☐ _____

☐ _____

☐ _____

☐ _____

Notes:

Weekly Planner

Most Important:
_____
_____
_____
_____

To Do List:
☐ _____
☐ _____
☐ _____
☐ _____
☐ _____
☐ _____
☐ _____

Monday

Goals: _____
_____
_____

Tuesday

Wednesday

Thursday

Friday

Saturday

Sunday

MONDAY

To Dos:

- [ ] _____
- [ ] _____
- [ ] _____
- [ ] _____
- [ ] _____
- [ ] _____

Notes:

_____
_____
_____
_____
_____
_____

TUESDAY

DATE: _____

To Dos:

- [ ] _____
- [ ] _____
- [ ] _____
- [ ] _____
- [ ] _____
- [ ] _____

Notes:

_____
_____
_____
_____
_____
_____

WEDNESDAY

DATE: _____

To Dos:

- [ ] _____
- [ ] _____
- [ ] _____
- [ ] _____
- [ ] _____
- [ ] _____

Notes:

_____
_____
_____
_____
_____
_____

THURSDAY

DATE: _____

To Dos:

- [ ] _____
- [ ] _____
- [ ] _____
- [ ] _____
- [ ] _____
- [ ] _____

Notes:

_____
_____
_____
_____
_____
_____

FRIDAY

To Dos:
- ☐ _____
- ☐ _____
- ☐ _____
- ☐ _____
- ☐ _____
- ☐ _____

Notes:
_____
_____
_____
_____
_____
_____

SATURDAY

DATE: _____

To Dos:
- ☐ _____
- ☐ _____
- ☐ _____
- ☐ _____
- ☐ _____
- ☐ _____

Notes:
_____
_____
_____
_____
_____
_____

SUNDAY

DATE: _____

To Dos:
- ☐ _____
- ☐ _____
- ☐ _____
- ☐ _____
- ☐ _____
- ☐ _____

Notes:
_____
_____
_____
_____
_____
_____

WEEKLY RECAP:

Rating: ☆☆☆☆☆

BEST PERFORMING POST:
_____
_____
_____

Platform: 🐦 👻 f in ♪ 📷 ▶ P

Posts:
☐	☐	☐	☐	☐	☐	☐	☐
☐	☐	☐	☐	☐	☐	☐	☐
☐	☐	☐	☐	☐	☐	☐	☐
☐	☐	☐	☐	☐	☐	☐	☐
☐	☐	☐	☐	☐	☐	☐	☐

Weekly Planner

Most Important:

_____
_____
_____
_____

To Do List:

☐ _____
☐ _____
☐ _____
☐ _____
☐ _____
☐ _____
☐ _____

Monday

Goals: _____
_____
_____

Tuesday

Wednesday

Thursday

Friday

Saturday

Sunday

MONDAY

To Dos:

☐ _____
☐ _____
☐ _____
☐ _____
☐ _____
☐ _____

Notes:

_____
_____
_____
_____
_____
_____

TUESDAY

DATE: _____

To Dos:

☐ _____
☐ _____
☐ _____
☐ _____
☐ _____
☐ _____

Notes:

_____
_____
_____
_____
_____
_____

WEDNESDAY

DATE: _____

To Dos:

☐ _____
☐ _____
☐ _____
☐ _____
☐ _____
☐ _____

Notes:

_____
_____
_____
_____
_____
_____

THURSDAY

DATE: _____

To Dos:

☐ _____
☐ _____
☐ _____
☐ _____
☐ _____
☐ _____

Notes:

_____
_____
_____
_____
_____
_____

FRIDAY

To Dos:
- ☐ _____
- ☐ _____
- ☐ _____
- ☐ _____
- ☐ _____
- ☐ _____

Notes:
_____
_____
_____
_____
_____

SATURDAY

DATE: _____

To Dos:
- ☐ _____
- ☐ _____
- ☐ _____
- ☐ _____
- ☐ _____
- ☐ _____

Notes:
_____
_____
_____
_____
_____

SUNDAY

DATE: _____

To Dos:
- ☐ _____
- ☐ _____
- ☐ _____
- ☐ _____
- ☐ _____
- ☐ _____

Notes:
_____
_____
_____
_____
_____
_____

WEEKLY RECAP:

Rating: ☆☆☆☆☆

BEST PERFORMING POST:
_____
_____

Platform: 🐦 👻 f in ♪ 📷 ▶ 𝓟

Posts:

🐦	👻	f	in	♪	📷	▶	𝓟
☐	☐	☐	☐	☐	☐	☐	☐
☐	☐	☐	☐	☐	☐	☐	☐
☐	☐	☐	☐	☐	☐	☐	☐
☐	☐	☐	☐	☐	☐	☐	☐
☐	☐	☐	☐	☐	☐	☐	☐

Weekly Planner

Most Important:

_____
_____
_____
_____
_____

To Do List:

☐ _____
☐ _____
☐ _____
☐ _____
☐ _____
☐ _____
☐ _____

Monday

Goals: _____
_____
_____

Tuesday	Wednesday

Thursday	Friday

Saturday	Sunday

MONDAY

To Dos:
- ☐ _____
- ☐ _____
- ☐ _____
- ☐ _____
- ☐ _____
- ☐ _____

Notes:
_____
_____
_____
_____
_____
_____

TUESDAY

DATE: _____

To Dos:
- ☐ _____
- ☐ _____
- ☐ _____
- ☐ _____
- ☐ _____
- ☐ _____

Notes:
_____
_____
_____
_____
_____
_____

WEDNESDAY

DATE: _____

To Dos:
- ☐ _____
- ☐ _____
- ☐ _____
- ☐ _____
- ☐ _____
- ☐ _____

Notes:
_____
_____
_____
_____
_____
_____

THURSDAY

DATE: _____

To Dos:
- ☐ _____
- ☐ _____
- ☐ _____
- ☐ _____
- ☐ _____
- ☐ _____

Notes:
_____
_____
_____
_____
_____
_____

FRIDAY

To Dos:
- [ ] _____
- [ ] _____
- [ ] _____
- [ ] _____
- [ ] _____
- [ ] _____

Notes:
_____
_____
_____
_____
_____
_____

SATURDAY

DATE: _____

To Dos:
- [ ] _____
- [ ] _____
- [ ] _____
- [ ] _____
- [ ] _____
- [ ] _____

Notes:
_____
_____
_____
_____
_____
_____

SUNDAY

DATE: _____

To Dos:
- [ ] _____
- [ ] _____
- [ ] _____
- [ ] _____
- [ ] _____
- [ ] _____

Notes:
_____
_____
_____
_____
_____
_____

WEEKLY RECAP:

Rating: ☆☆☆☆☆

BEST PERFORMING POST:
_____
_____
_____

Platform:

🐦	👻	f	in	♪	📷	▶	P
Posts:							
☐	☐	☐	☐	☐	☐	☐	☐
☐	☐	☐	☐	☐	☐	☐	☐
☐	☐	☐	☐	☐	☐	☐	☐
☐	☐	☐	☐	☐	☐	☐	☐
☐	☐	☐	☐	☐	☐	☐	☐

Weekly Planner

Most Important:

_____

_____

_____

_____

_____

To Do List:

☐ _____

☐ _____

☐ _____

☐ _____

☐ _____

☐ _____

☐ _____

Monday

Goals: _____

_____

_____

Tuesday

Wednesday

Thursday

Friday

Saturday

Sunday

MONDAY

To Dos:

☐ _____

☐ _____

☐ _____

☐ _____

☐ _____

☐ _____

Notes:

_____

_____

_____

_____

_____

_____

_____

TUESDAY

DATE: _____

To Dos:

☐ _____

☐ _____

☐ _____

☐ _____

☐ _____

☐ _____

Notes:

_____

_____

_____

_____

_____

_____

_____

WEDNESDAY

DATE: _____

To Dos:

☐ _____

☐ _____

☐ _____

☐ _____

☐ _____

☐ _____

Notes:

_____

_____

_____

_____

_____

_____

_____

THURSDAY

DATE: _____

To Dos:

☐ _____

☐ _____

☐ _____

☐ _____

☐ _____

☐ _____

Notes:

_____

_____

_____

_____

_____

_____

_____

FRIDAY

To Dos:

- [ ] _____
- [ ] _____
- [ ] _____
- [ ] _____
- [ ] _____
- [ ] _____

DATE: _____ WEEK: _____

Notes:

_____
_____
_____
_____
_____
_____

SATURDAY

To Dos:

- [ ] _____
- [ ] _____
- [ ] _____
- [ ] _____
- [ ] _____
- [ ] _____

DATE: _____

Notes:

_____
_____
_____
_____
_____
_____

SUNDAY

To Dos:

- [ ] _____
- [ ] _____
- [ ] _____
- [ ] _____
- [ ] _____
- [ ] _____

DATE: _____

Notes:

_____
_____
_____
_____
_____
_____

WEEKLY RECAP: **Platform:**

Rating: ☆☆☆☆☆ **Posts:**

BEST PERFORMING POST:

_____
_____

Weekly Planner

Most Important:

_____
_____
_____
_____

To Do List:

☐ _____
☐ _____
☐ _____
☐ _____
☐ _____
☐ _____
☐ _____

Monday

Goals: _____

_____
_____
_____

Tuesday

Wednesday

Thursday

Friday

Saturday

Sunday

MONDAY

To Dos:

☐ _____
☐ _____
☐ _____
☐ _____
☐ _____
☐ _____

Notes:

_____
_____
_____
_____
_____
_____

TUESDAY

DATE: _____

To Dos:

☐ _____
☐ _____
☐ _____
☐ _____
☐ _____
☐ _____

Notes:

_____
_____
_____
_____
_____
_____

WEDNESDAY

DATE: _____

To Dos:

☐ _____
☐ _____
☐ _____
☐ _____
☐ _____
☐ _____

Notes:

_____
_____
_____
_____
_____
_____

THURSDAY

DATE: _____

To Dos:

☐ _____
☐ _____
☐ _____
☐ _____
☐ _____
☐ _____

Notes:

_____
_____
_____
_____
_____
_____

FRIDAY

To Dos:
- [ ] _____
- [ ] _____
- [ ] _____
- [ ] _____
- [ ] _____
- [ ] _____

Notes:
_____
_____
_____
_____
_____
_____

SATURDAY

DATE: _____

To Dos:
- [ ] _____
- [ ] _____
- [ ] _____
- [ ] _____
- [ ] _____
- [ ] _____

Notes:
_____
_____
_____
_____
_____
_____

SUNDAY

DATE: _____

To Dos:
- [ ] _____
- [ ] _____
- [ ] _____
- [ ] _____
- [ ] _____
- [ ] _____

Notes:
_____
_____
_____
_____
_____
_____

WEEKLY RECAP:

Platform: 🐦 👻 f in ♪ 📷 ▶ P

Rating: ☆☆☆☆☆   **Posts:**

☐	☐	☐	☐	☐	☐	☐	☐
☐	☐	☐	☐	☐	☐	☐	☐
☐	☐	☐	☐	☐	☐	☐	☐
☐	☐	☐	☐	☐	☐	☐	☐
☐	☐	☐	☐	☐	☐	☐	☐

BEST PERFORMING POST:

_____
_____
_____

Monthly Planner

MON	TUE	WED	THU	FRI	SAT	SUN

Events:

_____

_____

_____

_____

_____

To Do List:

☐ _____

☐ _____

☐ _____

☐ _____

☐ _____

Notes:

Weekly Planner

Most Important:

_____

_____

_____

_____

To Do List:

☐ _____

☐ _____

☐ _____

☐ _____

☐ _____

☐ _____

☐ _____

Monday

Goals: _____

_____

_____

Tuesday

Wednesday

Thursday

Friday

Saturday

Sunday

MONDAY

To Dos:

☐ _____

☐ _____

☐ _____

☐ _____

☐ _____

☐ _____

Notes:

_____

_____

_____

_____

_____

_____

TUESDAY

DATE: _____

To Dos:

☐ _____

☐ _____

☐ _____

☐ _____

☐ _____

☐ _____

Notes:

_____

_____

_____

_____

_____

_____

WEDNESDAY

DATE: _____

To Dos:

☐ _____

☐ _____

☐ _____

☐ _____

☐ _____

☐ _____

Notes:

_____

_____

_____

_____

_____

_____

THURSDAY

DATE: _____

To Dos:

☐ _____

☐ _____

☐ _____

☐ _____

☐ _____

☐ _____

Notes:

_____

_____

_____

_____

_____

_____

FRIDAY

To Dos:
- [ ] _____
- [ ] _____
- [ ] _____
- [ ] _____
- [ ] _____
- [ ] _____

Notes:
_____
_____
_____
_____
_____

SATURDAY

DATE: _____

To Dos:
- [ ] _____
- [ ] _____
- [ ] _____
- [ ] _____
- [ ] _____
- [ ] _____

Notes:
_____
_____
_____
_____
_____

SUNDAY

DATE: _____

To Dos:
- [ ] _____
- [ ] _____
- [ ] _____
- [ ] _____
- [ ] _____
- [ ] _____

Notes:
_____
_____
_____
_____
_____

WEEKLY RECAP:

Rating: ☆☆☆☆☆

BEST PERFORMING POST:
_____
_____
_____

Platform: Twitter Snapchat Facebook LinkedIn TikTok Instagram YouTube Pinterest

Posts:

☐	☐	☐	☐	☐	☐	☐	☐
☐	☐	☐	☐	☐	☐	☐	☐
☐	☐	☐	☐	☐	☐	☐	☐
☐	☐	☐	☐	☐	☐	☐	☐
☐	☐	☐	☐	☐	☐	☐	☐

Weekly Planner

Most Important:

_____
_____
_____
_____

To Do List:

☐ _____
☐ _____
☐ _____
☐ _____
☐ _____
☐ _____
☐ _____

Goals: _____
_____
_____
_____

Monday

Tuesday	Wednesday

Thursday	Friday

Saturday	Sunday

MONDAY

To Dos:

☐ _____
☐ _____
☐ _____
☐ _____
☐ _____
☐ _____

Notes:

_____
_____
_____
_____
_____
_____
_____

TUESDAY

DATE: _____

To Dos:

☐ _____
☐ _____
☐ _____
☐ _____
☐ _____
☐ _____

Notes:

_____
_____
_____
_____
_____
_____
_____

WEDNESDAY

DATE: _____

To Dos:

☐ _____
☐ _____
☐ _____
☐ _____
☐ _____
☐ _____

Notes:

_____
_____
_____
_____
_____
_____
_____

THURSDAY

DATE: _____

To Dos:

☐ _____
☐ _____
☐ _____
☐ _____
☐ _____
☐ _____

Notes:

_____
_____
_____
_____
_____
_____
_____

FRIDAY

To Dos:

- [ ] _____
- [ ] _____
- [ ] _____
- [ ] _____
- [ ] _____
- [ ] _____

DATE: _____ WEEK: _____

Notes:

_____
_____
_____
_____
_____
_____

SATURDAY

To Dos:

- [ ] _____
- [ ] _____
- [ ] _____
- [ ] _____
- [ ] _____
- [ ] _____

DATE: _____

Notes:

_____
_____
_____
_____
_____
_____

SUNDAY

To Dos:

- [ ] _____
- [ ] _____
- [ ] _____
- [ ] _____
- [ ] _____
- [ ] _____

DATE: _____

Notes:

_____
_____
_____
_____
_____
_____

WEEKLY RECAP: **Platform:**

Rating: ☆☆☆☆☆   **Posts:**

BEST PERFORMING POST:

_____
_____
_____

Weekly Planner

Most Important:

_____
_____
_____
_____

To Do List:

☐ _____
☐ _____
☐ _____
☐ _____
☐ _____
☐ _____
☐ _____

Monday

Goals: _____

_____
_____

Tuesday

Wednesday

Thursday

Friday

Saturday

Sunday

MONDAY

To Dos:

☐ _____
☐ _____
☐ _____
☐ _____
☐ _____
☐ _____

Notes:

_____
_____
_____
_____
_____
_____
_____

TUESDAY

DATE: _____

To Dos:

☐ _____
☐ _____
☐ _____
☐ _____
☐ _____
☐ _____

Notes:

_____
_____
_____
_____
_____
_____
_____

WEDNESDAY

DATE: _____

To Dos:

☐ _____
☐ _____
☐ _____
☐ _____
☐ _____
☐ _____

Notes:

_____
_____
_____
_____
_____
_____
_____

THURSDAY

DATE: _____

To Dos:

☐ _____
☐ _____
☐ _____
☐ _____
☐ _____
☐ _____

Notes:

_____
_____
_____
_____
_____
_____

FRIDAY

DATE: _____ WEEK: _____

To Dos:

- [ ] _____
- [ ] _____
- [ ] _____
- [ ] _____
- [ ] _____
- [ ] _____

Notes:

_____
_____
_____
_____
_____
_____

SATURDAY

DATE: _____

To Dos:

- [ ] _____
- [ ] _____
- [ ] _____
- [ ] _____
- [ ] _____
- [ ] _____

Notes:

_____
_____
_____
_____
_____
_____

SUNDAY

DATE: _____

To Dos:

- [ ] _____
- [ ] _____
- [ ] _____
- [ ] _____
- [ ] _____
- [ ] _____

Notes:

_____
_____
_____
_____
_____
_____

WEEKLY RECAP: **Platform:**

Rating: ☆☆☆☆☆ **Posts:**

BEST PERFORMING POST:

_____
_____
_____

Platform	🐦	👻	f	in	♪	📷	▶	P
Posts:	☐	☐	☐	☐	☐	☐	☐	☐
	☐	☐	☐	☐	☐	☐	☐	☐
	☐	☐	☐	☐	☐	☐	☐	☐
	☐	☐	☐	☐	☐	☐	☐	☐
	☐	☐	☐	☐	☐	☐	☐	☐

Weekly Planner

Most Important:

_____

_____

_____

_____

To Do List:

☐ _____

☐ _____

☐ _____

☐ _____

☐ _____

☐ _____

☐ _____

Monday

Goals: _____

_____

_____

Tuesday

Wednesday

Thursday

Friday

Saturday

Sunday

MONDAY

To Dos:

- ☐ _____
- ☐ _____
- ☐ _____
- ☐ _____
- ☐ _____
- ☐ _____

Notes:

_____
_____
_____
_____
_____
_____

TUESDAY

DATE: _____

To Dos:

- ☐ _____
- ☐ _____
- ☐ _____
- ☐ _____
- ☐ _____
- ☐ _____

Notes:

_____
_____
_____
_____
_____
_____

WEDNESDAY

DATE: _____

To Dos:

- ☐ _____
- ☐ _____
- ☐ _____
- ☐ _____
- ☐ _____
- ☐ _____

Notes:

_____
_____
_____
_____
_____
_____

THURSDAY

DATE: _____

To Dos:

- ☐ _____
- ☐ _____
- ☐ _____
- ☐ _____
- ☐ _____
- ☐ _____

Notes:

_____
_____
_____
_____
_____
_____

FRIDAY

To Dos:
- [ ] _____
- [ ] _____
- [ ] _____
- [ ] _____
- [ ] _____
- [ ] _____

Notes:
_____
_____
_____
_____
_____

SATURDAY

DATE: _____

To Dos:
- [ ] _____
- [ ] _____
- [ ] _____
- [ ] _____
- [ ] _____
- [ ] _____

Notes:
_____
_____
_____
_____
_____
_____

SUNDAY

DATE: _____

To Dos:
- [ ] _____
- [ ] _____
- [ ] _____
- [ ] _____
- [ ] _____
- [ ] _____

Notes:
_____
_____
_____
_____
_____
_____

WEEKLY RECAP: **Platform:**

Rating: ☆☆☆☆☆ **Posts:**

BEST PERFORMING POST:
_____
_____
_____

Weekly Planner

Most Important:
_____
_____
_____
_____

To Do List:
☐ _____
☐ _____
☐ _____
☐ _____
☐ _____
☐ _____
☐ _____

Monday

Goals: _____
_____
_____

Tuesday	Wednesday

Thursday	Friday

Saturday	Sunday

MONDAY

To Dos:

☐ _____
☐ _____
☐ _____
☐ _____
☐ _____
☐ _____

DATE: _____ WEEK: _____

Notes:

_____
_____
_____
_____
_____
_____

TUESDAY

To Dos:

☐ _____
☐ _____
☐ _____
☐ _____
☐ _____
☐ _____

DATE: _____

Notes:

_____
_____
_____
_____
_____
_____

WEDNESDAY

To Dos:

☐ _____
☐ _____
☐ _____
☐ _____
☐ _____
☐ _____

DATE: _____

Notes:

_____
_____
_____
_____
_____
_____

THURSDAY

To Dos:

☐ _____
☐ _____
☐ _____
☐ _____
☐ _____
☐ _____

DATE: _____

Notes:

_____
_____
_____
_____
_____
_____

FRIDAY

DATE: _____ WEEK: _____

To Dos:
- [ ] _____
- [ ] _____
- [ ] _____
- [ ] _____
- [ ] _____
- [ ] _____

Notes:
_____
_____
_____
_____
_____

SATURDAY

DATE: _____

To Dos:
- [ ] _____
- [ ] _____
- [ ] _____
- [ ] _____
- [ ] _____
- [ ] _____

Notes:
_____
_____
_____
_____
_____

SUNDAY

DATE: _____

To Dos:
- [ ] _____
- [ ] _____
- [ ] _____
- [ ] _____
- [ ] _____
- [ ] _____

Notes:
_____
_____
_____
_____
_____

WEEKLY RECAP: **Platform:**

Rating: ☆☆☆☆☆ **Posts:**

BEST PERFORMING POST:

_____
_____

Content Planner

Post Title: _____

Keywords: _____

Hashtags: _____

Content Details:

Notes:

_____

_____

_____

_____

_____

_____

_____

_____

_____

To Do List:

☐ Brainstorm Content

☐ Graphic Creation

☐ Affiliate & Sponsor Links

☐ Call to Action

☐ Grammar Check

☐ Link Check

☐ Post Scheduling

☐ Post Premiere

☐ _____

☐ _____

Results:

♥ _____   🗨 _____   👤 _____   ◹ _____   ⊞ _____

Rating: ☆☆☆☆☆   **Time Posted:** _____   **Engagement Rate:** _____

Notes: _____

Content Planner

Post Title: _____

Keywords: _____

Hashtags: _____

Content Details:

Notes:

_____

_____

_____

_____

_____

_____

_____

_____

_____

To Do List:

☐ Brainstorm Content

☐ Graphic Creation

☐ Affiliate & Sponsor Links

☐ Call to Action

☐ Grammar Check

☐ Link Check

☐ Post Scheduling

☐ Post Premiere

☐ _____

☐ _____

Results:

♥ _____   🗨 _____   👤 _____   ◹ _____   🔖 _____

Rating: ☆☆☆☆☆   **Time Posted:** _____   **Engagement Rate:** _____

Notes: _____

_____

Content Planner

Post Title: _____

Keywords: _____

Hashtags: _____

Content Details:

Notes:

_____

_____

_____

_____

_____

_____

_____

_____

_____

To Do List:

- ☐ Brainstorm Content
- ☐ Graphic Creation
- ☐ Affiliate & Sponsor Links
- ☐ Call to Action
- ☐ Grammar Check
- ☐ Link Check
- ☐ Post Scheduling
- ☐ Post Premiere
- ☐ _____
- ☐ _____

Results:

♥ _____   💬 _____   👤 _____   ⊿ _____   🔖 _____

Rating: ☆☆☆☆☆   **Time Posted:** _____   **Engagement Rate:** _____

Notes: _____

Content Planner

Post Title: _____

Keywords: _____

Hashtags: _____

Content Details:

Notes:

_____
_____
_____
_____
_____
_____
_____
_____
_____
_____

To Do List:

☐ Brainstorm Content
☐ Graphic Creation
☐ Affiliate & Sponsor Links
☐ Call to Action
☐ Grammar Check
☐ Link Check
☐ Post Scheduling
☐ Post Premiere
☐ _____
☐ _____

Results:

♥ _____ 💬 _____ 👤 _____ ▽ _____ 🔖 _____

Rating: ☆☆☆☆☆   **Time Posted:** _____   **Engagement Rate:** _____

Notes: _____

_____

Content Planner

Post Title: _____

Keywords: _____

Hashtags: _____

Content Details:

Notes:

_____

_____

_____

_____

_____

_____

_____

_____

_____

_____

_____

To Do List:

☐ Brainstorm Content

☐ Graphic Creation

☐ Affiliate & Sponsor Links

☐ Call to Action

☐ Grammar Check

☐ Link Check

☐ Post Scheduling

☐ Post Premiere

☐ _____

☐ _____

Results:

♥ _____   💬 _____   👤 _____   ✈ _____   ⊞ _____

Rating: ☆☆☆☆☆   **Time Posted:** _____   **Engagement Rate:** _____

Notes: _____

Content Planner

Post Title: _____

Keywords: _____

Hashtags: _____

Content Details:

Notes:

_____

_____

_____

_____

_____

_____

_____

_____

_____

_____

To Do List:

☐ Brainstorm Content

☐ Graphic Creation

☐ Affiliate & Sponsor Links

☐ Call to Action

☐ Grammar Check

☐ Link Check

☐ Post Scheduling

☐ Post Premiere

☐ _____

☐ _____

Results:

♥ _____   💬 _____   👤 _____   ◹ _____   🔖 _____

Rating: ☆☆☆☆☆   **Time Posted:** _____   **Engagement Rate:** _____

Notes: _____

_____

Content Planner

Post Title: _____

Keywords: _____

Hashtags: _____

Content Details:

Notes:

_____

_____

_____

_____

_____

_____

_____

_____

_____

To Do List:

- ☐ Brainstorm Content
- ☐ Graphic Creation
- ☐ Affiliate & Sponsor Links
- ☐ Call to Action
- ☐ Grammar Check
- ☐ Link Check
- ☐ Post Scheduling
- ☐ Post Premiere
- ☐ _____
- ☐ _____

Results:

♥ _____   💬 _____   👤 _____   ✈ _____   🔖 _____

Rating: ☆☆☆☆☆   **Time Posted:** _____   **Engagement Rate:** _____

Notes: _____

Content Planner

Post Title: _____

Keywords: _____
Hashtags: _____

Content Details:

Notes:

_____
_____
_____
_____
_____
_____
_____
_____
_____

To Do List:

☐ Brainstorm Content
☐ Graphic Creation
☐ Affiliate & Sponsor Links
☐ Call to Action
☐ Grammar Check
☐ Link Check
☐ Post Scheduling
☐ Post Premiere
☐ _____
☐ _____

Results:

♥ _____   💬 _____   👤 _____   ➤ _____   🔖 _____

Rating: ☆☆☆☆☆   **Time Posted:** _____   **Engagement Rate:** _____

Notes: _____
_____

Content Planner

Post Title: _____

Keywords: _____

Hashtags: _____

Content Details:

Notes:	To Do List:

Notes:

_____

_____

_____

_____

_____

_____

_____

_____

_____

_____

To Do List:

☐ Brainstorm Content

☐ Graphic Creation

☐ Affiliate & Sponsor Links

☐ Call to Action

☐ Grammar Check

☐ Link Check

☐ Post Scheduling

☐ Post Premiere

☐ _____

☐ _____

Results:

♥ _____ 💬 _____ 👤 _____ ✈ _____ ⊞ _____

Rating: ☆☆☆☆☆ **Time Posted:** _____ **Engagement Rate:** _____

Notes: _____

Content Planner

Post Title: _____

Keywords: _____

Hashtags: _____

Content Details:

Notes:

_____

_____

_____

_____

_____

_____

_____

_____

_____

_____

To Do List:

☐ Brainstorm Content

☐ Graphic Creation

☐ Affiliate & Sponsor Links

☐ Call to Action

☐ Grammar Check

☐ Link Check

☐ Post Scheduling

☐ Post Premiere

☐ _____

☐ _____

Results:

♥ _____ 💬 _____ 👤 _____ ✈ _____ 🔖 _____

Rating: ☆☆☆☆☆ **Time Posted:** _____ **Engagement Rate:** _____

Notes: _____

_____

Content Planner

Date:

Post Title: _____

Keywords: _____

Hashtags: _____

Content Details:

Notes:

_____

_____

_____

_____

_____

_____

_____

_____

_____

To Do List:

☐ Brainstorm Content

☐ Graphic Creation

☐ Affiliate & Sponsor Links

☐ Call to Action

☐ Grammar Check

☐ Link Check

☐ Post Scheduling

☐ Post Premiere

☐ _____

☐ _____

Results:

♥ _____ 💬 _____ 👤 _____ ◹ _____ 🔖 _____

Rating: ☆☆☆☆☆   **Time Posted:** _____   **Engagement Rate:** _____

Notes: _____

Content Planner

Post Title: _____

Keywords: _____

Hashtags: _____

Content Details:

Notes:

_____

_____

_____

_____

_____

_____

_____

_____

_____

To Do List:

☐ Brainstorm Content

☐ Graphic Creation

☐ Affiliate & Sponsor Links

☐ Call to Action

☐ Grammar Check

☐ Link Check

☐ Post Scheduling

☐ Post Premiere

☐ _____

☐ _____

Results:

♥ _____   💬 _____   👤 _____   ◺ _____   🔖 _____

Rating: ☆☆☆☆☆   **Time Posted:** _____   **Engagement Rate:** _____

Notes: _____

_____

Content Planner

Post Title: _____

Keywords: _____

Hashtags: _____

Content Details:

Notes:

_____

_____

_____

_____

_____

_____

_____

_____

To Do List:

☐ Brainstorm Content

☐ Graphic Creation

☐ Affiliate & Sponsor Links

☐ Call to Action

☐ Grammar Check

☐ Link Check

☐ Post Scheduling

☐ Post Premiere

☐ _____

☐ _____

Results:

♥ _____   💬 _____   👤 _____   ◹ _____   🔖 _____

Rating: ☆☆☆☆☆   **Time Posted:** _____   **Engagement Rate:** _____

Notes: _____

Content Planner

Post Title: _____

Keywords: _____

Hashtags: _____

Content Details:

Notes:

_____
_____
_____
_____
_____
_____
_____
_____

To Do List:

☐ Brainstorm Content
☐ Graphic Creation
☐ Affiliate & Sponsor Links
☐ Call to Action
☐ Grammar Check
☐ Link Check
☐ Post Scheduling
☐ Post Premiere
☐ _____
☐ _____

Results:

♥ _____ 💬 _____ 👤 _____ ⊿ _____ 🔖 _____

Rating: ☆☆☆☆☆ **Time Posted:** _____ **Engagement Rate:** _____

Notes: _____

Content Planner

Post Title: _____

Keywords: _____

Hashtags: _____

Content Details:

Notes:

_____

_____

_____

_____

_____

_____

_____

_____

_____

To Do List:

☐ Brainstorm Content

☐ Graphic Creation

☐ Affiliate & Sponsor Links

☐ Call to Action

☐ Grammar Check

☐ Link Check

☐ Post Scheduling

☐ Post Premiere

☐ _____

☐ _____

Results:

♥ _____   💬 _____   👤 _____   ⏶ _____   ⊞ _____

Rating: ☆ ☆ ☆ ☆ ☆   **Time Posted:** _____   **Engagement Rate:** _____

Notes: _____

Content Planner

Post Title: _____

Keywords: _____

Hashtags: _____

Content Details:

Notes:

_____

_____

_____

_____

_____

_____

_____

_____

_____

To Do List:

☐ Brainstorm Content _____

☐ Graphic Creation _____

☐ Affiliate & Sponsor Links _____

☐ Call to Action _____

☐ Grammar Check _____

☐ Link Check _____

☐ Post Scheduling _____

☐ Post Premiere _____

☐ _____

☐ _____

Results:

♥ _____   💬 _____   👤 _____   ✈ _____   🔖 _____

Rating: ☆☆☆☆☆   **Time Posted:** _____   **Engagement Rate:** _____

Notes: _____

_____

Content Planner

Post Title: _____

Keywords: _____

Hashtags: _____

```
+--------------------------------------------------+
|                 Content Details:                 |
|                                                  |
|                                                  |
|                                                  |
|                                                  |
|                                                  |
|                                                  |
|                                                  |
|                                                  |
|                                                  |
+--------------------------------------------------+
```

Notes: To Do List:

_____   ☐ Brainstorm Content

_____   ☐ Graphic Creation

_____   ☐ Affiliate & Sponsor Links

_____   ☐ Call to Action

_____   ☐ Grammar Check

_____   ☐ Link Check

_____   ☐ Post Scheduling

_____   ☐ Post Premiere

_____   ☐ _____

_____   ☐ _____

Results:

♥ _____   💬 _____   👤 _____   ◹ _____   🔖 _____

Rating: ☆☆☆☆☆   **Time Posted:** _____   **Engagement Rate:** _____

Notes: _____

Content Planner

Post Title: _____

Keywords: _____

Hashtags: _____

Content Details:

Notes:

_____

_____

_____

_____

_____

_____

_____

_____

_____

_____

To Do List:

☐ Brainstorm Content _____

☐ Graphic Creation _____

☐ Affiliate & Sponsor Links _____

☐ Call to Action _____

☐ Grammar Check _____

☐ Link Check _____

☐ Post Scheduling _____

☐ Post Premiere _____

☐ _____

☐ _____

Results:

♥ _____   💬 _____   👤 _____   ◹ _____   🔖 _____

Rating: ☆☆☆☆☆   **Time Posted:** _____   **Engagement Rate:** _____

Notes: _____

_____

Content Planner

Post Title: _____

Keywords: _____

Hashtags: _____

Content Details:

Notes:

_____

_____

_____

_____

_____

_____

_____

_____

_____

To Do List:

☐ Brainstorm Content

☐ Graphic Creation

☐ Affiliate & Sponsor Links

☐ Call to Action

☐ Grammar Check

☐ Link Check

☐ Post Scheduling

☐ Post Premiere

☐ _____

☐ _____

Results:

♥ _____ 💬 _____ 👤 _____ ✈ _____ 🔖 _____

Rating: ☆☆☆☆☆ **Time Posted:** _____ **Engagement Rate:** _____

Notes: _____

Content Planner

Post Title: _____

Keywords: _____

Hashtags: _____

Content Details:

Notes:

_____

_____

_____

_____

_____

_____

_____

_____

_____

_____

To Do List:

☐ Brainstorm Content

☐ Graphic Creation

☐ Affiliate & Sponsor Links

☐ Call to Action

☐ Grammar Check

☐ Link Check

☐ Post Scheduling

☐ Post Premiere

☐ _____

☐ _____

Results:

♥ _____   ● _____   👤 _____   ◁ _____   🔖 _____

Rating: ☆☆☆☆☆   **Time Posted:** _____   **Engagement Rate:** _____

Notes: _____

_____

Content Planner

Post Title: _____

Keywords: _____

Hashtags: _____

Content Details:

Notes:

_____

_____

_____

_____

_____

_____

_____

_____

_____

_____

To Do List:

☐ Brainstorm Content

☐ Graphic Creation

☐ Affiliate & Sponsor Links

☐ Call to Action

☐ Grammar Check

☐ Link Check

☐ Post Scheduling

☐ Post Premiere

☐ _____

☐ _____

Results:

♥ _____   💬 _____   👤 _____   ◸ _____   ⊞ _____

Rating: ☆☆☆☆☆   **Time Posted:** _____   **Engagement Rate:** _____

Notes: _____

Content Planner

Post Title: _____

Keywords: _____

Hashtags: _____

Content Details:

Notes:

_____

_____

_____

_____

_____

_____

_____

_____

_____

To Do List:

☐ Brainstorm Content _____

☐ Graphic Creation _____

☐ Affiliate & Sponsor Links _____

☐ Call to Action _____

☐ Grammar Check _____

☐ Link Check _____

☐ Post Scheduling _____

☐ Post Premiere _____

☐ _____

☐ _____

Results:

♥ _____   💬 _____   👤 _____   ⏎ _____   🔖 _____

Rating: ☆☆☆☆☆   **Time Posted:** _____   **Engagement Rate:** _____

Notes: _____

Content Planner

Post Title: _____

Keywords: _____

Hashtags: _____

Content Details:

Notes:

_____

_____

_____

_____

_____

_____

_____

_____

_____

_____

To Do List:

☐ Brainstorm Content

☐ Graphic Creation

☐ Affiliate & Sponsor Links

☐ Call to Action

☐ Grammar Check

☐ Link Check

☐ Post Scheduling

☐ Post Premiere

☐ _____

☐ _____

Results:

♥ _____   💬 _____   👤 _____   ✈ _____   🔖 _____

Rating: ☆☆☆☆☆   **Time Posted:** _____   **Engagement Rate:** _____

Notes: _____

Content Planner

Post Title: _____

Keywords: _____

Hashtags: _____

Content Details:

Notes:

_____

_____

_____

_____

_____

_____

_____

_____

_____

To Do List:

☐ Brainstorm Content _____

☐ Graphic Creation _____

☐ Affiliate & Sponsor Links _____

☐ Call to Action _____

☐ Grammar Check _____

☐ Link Check _____

☐ Post Scheduling _____

☐ Post Premiere _____

☐ _____

☐ _____

Results:

♥ _____   💬 _____   👤 _____   ◹ _____   🔖 _____

Rating: ☆☆☆☆☆   **Time Posted:** _____   **Engagement Rate:** _____

Notes: _____

_____

Content Planner

Post Title: _____

Keywords: _____

Hashtags: _____

Content Details:

Notes:

_____

_____

_____

_____

_____

_____

_____

_____

_____

To Do List:

☐ Brainstorm Content

☐ Graphic Creation

☐ Affiliate & Sponsor Links

☐ Call to Action

☐ Grammar Check

☐ Link Check

☐ Post Scheduling

☐ Post Premiere

☐ _____

☐ _____

Results:

❤ _____ 💬 _____ 👤 _____ ➤ _____ 🔖 _____

Rating: ☆☆☆☆☆   **Time Posted:** _____   **Engagement Rate:** _____

Notes: _____

_____

Content Planner

Date:

Post Title: _____

Keywords: _____

Hashtags: _____

Content Details:

Notes:

_____
_____
_____
_____
_____
_____
_____
_____
_____

To Do List:

☐ Brainstorm Content
☐ Graphic Creation
☐ Affiliate & Sponsor Links
☐ Call to Action
☐ Grammar Check
☐ Link Check
☐ Post Scheduling
☐ Post Premiere
☐ _____
☐ _____

Results:

♥ _____ 💬 _____ 👤 _____ ◿ _____ 🔖 _____

Rating: ☆☆☆☆☆ **Time Posted:** _____ **Engagement Rate:** _____

Notes: _____

_____

Content Planner

Post Title: _____

Keywords: _____

Hashtags: _____

Content Details:

_____

Notes:

_____

_____

_____

_____

_____

_____

_____

_____

_____

_____

To Do List:

☐ Brainstorm Content

☐ Graphic Creation

☐ Affiliate & Sponsor Links

☐ Call to Action

☐ Grammar Check

☐ Link Check

☐ Post Scheduling

☐ Post Premiere

☐ _____

☐ _____

Results:

❤ _____ 💬 _____ 👤 _____ ▽ _____ 🔖 _____

Rating: ☆☆☆☆☆ **Time Posted:** _____ **Engagement Rate:** _____

Notes: _____

Content Planner

Post Title: _____

Keywords: _____

Hashtags: _____

Content Details:

Notes: | To Do List:

_____   ☐ Brainstorm Content

_____   ☐ Graphic Creation

_____   ☐ Affiliate & Sponsor Links

_____   ☐ Call to Action

_____   ☐ Grammar Check

_____   ☐ Link Check

_____   ☐ Post Scheduling

_____   ☐ Post Premiere

_____   ☐ _____

_____   ☐ _____

Results:

♥ _____   💬 _____   👤 _____   ➤ _____   🔖 _____

Rating: ☆☆☆☆☆   **Time Posted:** _____   **Engagement Rate:** _____

Notes: _____

_____

Content Planner

Post Title: _____

Keywords: _____

Hashtags: _____

Content Details:

Notes:

_____

_____

_____

_____

_____

_____

_____

_____

_____

To Do List:

☐ Brainstorm Content

☐ Graphic Creation

☐ Affiliate & Sponsor Links

☐ Call to Action

☐ Grammar Check

☐ Link Check

☐ Post Scheduling

☐ Post Premiere

☐ _____

☐ _____

Results:

♥ _____   💬 _____   👤 _____   ◁ _____   🔖 _____

Rating: ☆☆☆☆☆   **Time Posted:** _____   **Engagement Rate:** _____

Notes: _____

Content Planner

Post Title: _____

Keywords: _____

Hashtags: _____

Content Details:

Notes:

_____

_____

_____

_____

_____

_____

_____

_____

_____

_____

To Do List:

☐ Brainstorm Content _____

☐ Graphic Creation _____

☐ Affiliate & Sponsor Links _____

☐ Call to Action _____

☐ Grammar Check _____

☐ Link Check _____

☐ Post Scheduling _____

☐ Post Premiere _____

☐ _____

☐ _____

Results:

♥ _____   💬 _____   👤 _____   ✈ _____   🔖 _____

Rating: ☆☆☆☆☆   **Time Posted:** _____   **Engagement Rate:** _____

Notes: _____

_____

Content Planner

Post Title: _____

Keywords: _____

Hashtags: _____

Content Details:

Notes:

_____

_____

_____

_____

_____

_____

_____

_____

_____

To Do List:

☐ Brainstorm Content

☐ Graphic Creation

☐ Affiliate & Sponsor Links

☐ Call to Action

☐ Grammar Check

☐ Link Check

☐ Post Scheduling

☐ Post Premiere

☐ _____

☐ _____

Results:

♥ _____   💬 _____   👤 _____   ✈ _____   🔖 _____

Rating: ☆☆☆☆☆   **Time Posted:** _____   **Engagement Rate:** _____

Notes: _____

Content Planner

Post Title: _____

Keywords: _____

Hashtags: _____

Content Details:

Notes:

To Do List:

_____

_____

_____

_____

_____

_____

_____

_____

_____

_____

- ☐ Brainstorm Content
- ☐ Graphic Creation
- ☐ Affiliate & Sponsor Links
- ☐ Call to Action
- ☐ Grammar Check
- ☐ Link Check
- ☐ Post Scheduling
- ☐ Post Premiere
- ☐ _____
- ☐ _____

Results:

♥ _____   🗨 _____   👤 _____   ✈ _____   🔖 _____

Rating: ☆☆☆☆☆ **Time Posted:** _____ **Engagement Rate:** _____

Notes: _____

_____

Content Planner

Post Title: _____

Keywords: _____

Hashtags: _____

Content Details:

Notes:

_____

_____

_____

_____

_____

_____

_____

_____

_____

To Do List:

☐ Brainstorm Content

☐ Graphic Creation

☐ Affiliate & Sponsor Links

☐ Call to Action

☐ Grammar Check

☐ Link Check

☐ Post Scheduling

☐ Post Premiere

☐ _____

☐ _____

Results:

♥ _____   💬 _____   👤 _____   ✈ _____   🔖 _____

Rating: ☆☆☆☆☆   **Time Posted:** _____   **Engagement Rate:** _____

Notes: _____

_____

Content Planner

Post Title: _____

Keywords: _____

Hashtags: _____

Content Details:

Notes:

_____

_____

_____

_____

_____

_____

_____

_____

_____

_____

To Do List:

☐ Brainstorm Content

☐ Graphic Creation

☐ Affiliate & Sponsor Links

☐ Call to Action

☐ Grammar Check

☐ Link Check

☐ Post Scheduling

☐ Post Premiere

☐ _____

☐ _____

Results:

♥ _____ 💬 _____ 👤 _____ ◸ _____ 🔖 _____

Rating: ☆☆☆☆☆ **Time Posted:** _____ **Engagement Rate:** _____

Notes: _____

_____

Content Planner

Post Title: _____

Keywords: _____

Hashtags: _____

Content Details:

Notes:

_____

_____

_____

_____

_____

_____

_____

_____

_____

To Do List:

☐ Brainstorm Content

☐ Graphic Creation

☐ Affiliate & Sponsor Links

☐ Call to Action

☐ Grammar Check

☐ Link Check

☐ Post Scheduling

☐ Post Premiere

☐ _____

☐ _____

Results:

♥ _____ 💬 _____ 👤 _____ ✈ _____ 🔖 _____

Rating: ☆☆☆☆☆ **Time Posted:** _____ **Engagement Rate:** _____

Notes: _____

Content Planner

Post Title: _____

Keywords: _____

Hashtags: _____

Content Details:

Notes:

_____

_____

_____

_____

_____

_____

_____

_____

_____

_____

_____

To Do List:

☐ Brainstorm Content

☐ Graphic Creation

☐ Affiliate & Sponsor Links

☐ Call to Action

☐ Grammar Check

☐ Link Check

☐ Post Scheduling

☐ Post Premiere

☐ _____

☐ _____

Results:

♥ _____ 💬 _____ 👤 _____ ✈ _____ 🔖 _____

Rating: ☆☆☆☆☆ **Time Posted:** _____ **Engagement Rate:** _____

Notes: _____

_____

Content Planner

Post Title: _____

Keywords: _____

Hashtags: _____

Content Details:

Notes:

_____

_____

_____

_____

_____

_____

_____

_____

_____

To Do List:

☐ Brainstorm Content

☐ Graphic Creation

☐ Affiliate & Sponsor Links

☐ Call to Action

☐ Grammar Check

☐ Link Check

☐ Post Scheduling

☐ Post Premiere

☐ _____

☐ _____

Results:

♥ _____   💬 _____   👤 _____   ⧨ _____   🔖 _____

Rating: ☆☆☆☆☆   **Time Posted:** _____   **Engagement Rate:** _____

Notes: _____

Content Planner

Post Title: _____

Keywords: _____

Hashtags: _____

Content Details:

Notes:

_____

_____

_____

_____

_____

_____

_____

_____

_____

To Do List:

☐ Brainstorm Content

☐ Graphic Creation

☐ Affiliate & Sponsor Links

☐ Call to Action

☐ Grammar Check

☐ Link Check

☐ Post Scheduling

☐ Post Premiere

☐ _____

☐ _____

Results:

♥ _____   💬 _____   👤 _____   ◿ _____   🔖 _____

Rating: ☆☆☆☆☆   **Time Posted:** _____   **Engagement Rate:** _____

Notes: _____

_____

Content Planner

Post Title: _____

Keywords: _____

Hashtags: _____

Content Details:

Notes:

_____

_____

_____

_____

_____

_____

_____

_____

_____

To Do List:

☐ Brainstorm Content

☐ Graphic Creation

☐ Affiliate & Sponsor Links

☐ Call to Action

☐ Grammar Check

☐ Link Check

☐ Post Scheduling

☐ Post Premiere

☐ _____

☐ _____

Results:

♥ _____   💬 _____   👤 _____   ◹ _____   🔖 _____

Rating: ☆☆☆☆☆   **Time Posted:** _____   **Engagement Rate:** _____

Notes: _____

Content Planner

Post Title: _____

Keywords: _____

Hashtags: _____

Content Details:

Notes:

_____

_____

_____

_____

_____

_____

_____

_____

_____

To Do List:

☐ Brainstorm Content

☐ Graphic Creation

☐ Affiliate & Sponsor Links

☐ Call to Action

☐ Grammar Check

☐ Link Check

☐ Post Scheduling

☐ Post Premiere

☐ _____

☐ _____

Results:

♥ _____   💬 _____   👤 _____   ⊿ _____   🔖 _____

Rating: ☆☆☆☆☆   **Time Posted:** _____   **Engagement Rate:** _____

Notes: _____

_____

Content Planner

Post Title: _____

Keywords: _____

Hashtags: _____

Content Details:

Notes:

_____

_____

_____

_____

_____

_____

_____

_____

_____

To Do List:

☐ Brainstorm Content

☐ Graphic Creation

☐ Affiliate & Sponsor Links

☐ Call to Action

☐ Grammar Check

☐ Link Check

☐ Post Scheduling

☐ Post Premiere

☐ _____

☐ _____

Results:

♥ _____   💬 _____   👤 _____   ✈ _____   🔖 _____

Rating: ☆☆☆☆☆   **Time Posted:** _____   **Engagement Rate:** _____

Notes: _____

_____

Content Planner

Post Title: _____

Keywords: _____

Hashtags: _____

Content Details:

Notes:

_____

_____

_____

_____

_____

_____

_____

_____

_____

_____

To Do List:

☐ Brainstorm Content _____

☐ Graphic Creation _____

☐ Affiliate & Sponsor Links _____

☐ Call to Action _____

☐ Grammar Check _____

☐ Link Check _____

☐ Post Scheduling _____

☐ Post Premiere _____

☐ _____

☐ _____

Results:

♥ _____   💬 _____   👤 _____   ◁ _____   ⊞ _____

Rating: ☆☆☆☆☆   **Time Posted:** _____   **Engagement Rate:** _____

Notes: _____

Content Planner

Post Title: _____

Keywords: _____

Hashtags: _____

Content Details:

Notes:

_____

_____

_____

_____

_____

_____

_____

_____

_____

To Do List:

- ☐ Brainstorm Content
- ☐ Graphic Creation
- ☐ Affiliate & Sponsor Links
- ☐ Call to Action
- ☐ Grammar Check
- ☐ Link Check
- ☐ Post Scheduling
- ☐ Post Premiere
- ☐ _____
- ☐ _____

Results:

♥ _____   💬 _____   👤 _____   ✈ _____   🔖 _____

Rating: ☆☆☆☆☆   **Time Posted:** _____   **Engagement Rate:** _____

Notes: _____

Content Planner

Post Title: _____

Keywords: _____

Hashtags: _____

Content Details:

Notes:

_____

_____

_____

_____

_____

_____

_____

_____

_____

To Do List:

☐ Brainstorm Content

☐ Graphic Creation

☐ Affiliate & Sponsor Links

☐ Call to Action

☐ Grammar Check

☐ Link Check

☐ Post Scheduling

☐ Post Premiere

☐ _____

☐ _____

Results:

♥ _____   💬 _____   👤 _____   ✈ _____   🔖 _____

Rating: ☆☆☆☆☆   **Time Posted:** _____   **Engagement Rate:** _____

Notes: _____

_____

Content Planner

Post Title: _____

Keywords: _____

Hashtags: _____

Content Details:

Notes:

_____

_____

_____

_____

_____

_____

_____

_____

_____

To Do List:

☐ Brainstorm Content _____

☐ Graphic Creation _____

☐ Affiliate & Sponsor Links _____

☐ Call to Action _____

☐ Grammar Check _____

☐ Link Check _____

☐ Post Scheduling _____

☐ Post Premiere _____

☐ _____

☐ _____

Results:

♥ _____   💬 _____   👤 _____   ✈ _____   🔖 _____

Rating: ☆☆☆☆☆   **Time Posted:** _____   **Engagement Rate:** _____

Notes: _____

Content Planner

Post Title: _____

Keywords: _____

Hashtags: _____

Content Details:

Notes:

_____

_____

_____

_____

_____

_____

_____

_____

_____

To Do List:

☐ Brainstorm Content _____

☐ Graphic Creation _____

☐ Affiliate & Sponsor Links _____

☐ Call to Action _____

☐ Grammar Check _____

☐ Link Check _____

☐ Post Scheduling _____

☐ Post Premiere _____

☐ _____

☐ _____

Results:

♥ _____   💬 _____   👤 _____   ✈ _____   🔖 _____

Rating: ☆☆☆☆☆   **Time Posted:** _____   **Engagement Rate:** _____

Notes: _____

_____

Content Planner

Post Title: _____

Keywords: _____

Hashtags: _____

Content Details:

Notes:

_____

_____

_____

_____

_____

_____

_____

_____

_____

_____

To Do List:

☐ Brainstorm Content

☐ Graphic Creation

☐ Affiliate & Sponsor Links

☐ Call to Action

☐ Grammar Check

☐ Link Check

☐ Post Scheduling

☐ Post Premiere

☐ _____

☐ _____

Results:

♥ _____   💬 _____   👤 _____   ◹ _____   🔖 _____

Rating: ☆☆☆☆☆   **Time Posted:** _____   **Engagement Rate:** _____

Notes: _____

Content Planner

Post Title: _____

Keywords: _____

Hashtags: _____

Content Details:

Notes:

_____

_____

_____

_____

_____

_____

_____

_____

_____

_____

To Do List:

☐ Brainstorm Content

☐ Graphic Creation

☐ Affiliate & Sponsor Links

☐ Call to Action

☐ Grammar Check

☐ Link Check

☐ Post Scheduling

☐ Post Premiere

☐ _____

☐ _____

Results:

♥ _____   💬 _____   👤 _____   ✈ _____   🔖 _____

Rating: ☆☆☆☆☆   **Time Posted:** _____   **Engagement Rate:** _____

Notes: _____

_____

Content Planner

Post Title: _____

Keywords: _____

Hashtags: _____

Content Details:

Notes:

_____

_____

_____

_____

_____

_____

_____

_____

_____

_____

To Do List:

☐ Brainstorm Content

☐ Graphic Creation

☐ Affiliate & Sponsor Links

☐ Call to Action

☐ Grammar Check

☐ Link Check

☐ Post Scheduling

☐ Post Premiere

☐ _____

☐ _____

Results:

♥ _____ 💬 _____ 👤 _____ ◹ _____ ⊞ _____

Rating: ☆☆☆☆☆   **Time Posted:** _____   **Engagement Rate:** _____

Notes: _____

Content Planner

Post Title: _____
Keywords: _____
Hashtags: _____

Content Details:

Notes:

_____
_____
_____
_____
_____
_____
_____
_____
_____

To Do List:

☐ Brainstorm Content
☐ Graphic Creation
☐ Affiliate & Sponsor Links
☐ Call to Action
☐ Grammar Check
☐ Link Check
☐ Post Scheduling
☐ Post Premiere
☐
☐

Results:

♥ _____   💬 _____   👤 _____   ✈ _____   🔖 _____

Rating: ☆☆☆☆☆   **Time Posted:** _____   **Engagement Rate:** _____
Notes: _____

Content Planner

Post Title: _____

Keywords: _____

Hashtags: _____

Content Details:

Notes:

_____

_____

_____

_____

_____

_____

_____

_____

_____

_____

To Do List:

☐ Brainstorm Content

☐ Graphic Creation

☐ Affiliate & Sponsor Links

☐ Call to Action

☐ Grammar Check

☐ Link Check

☐ Post Scheduling

☐ Post Premiere

☐ _____

☐ _____

Results:

♥ _____   💬 _____   👤 _____   ⊿ _____   🔖 _____

Rating: ☆☆☆☆☆   **Time Posted:** _____   **Engagement Rate:** _____

Notes: _____

Content Planner

Post Title: _____

Keywords: _____

Hashtags: _____

Content Details:

Notes:

_____

_____

_____

_____

_____

_____

_____

_____

_____

_____

To Do List:

☐ Brainstorm Content _____

☐ Graphic Creation _____

☐ Affiliate & Sponsor Links _____

☐ Call to Action _____

☐ Grammar Check _____

☐ Link Check _____

☐ Post Scheduling _____

☐ Post Premiere _____

☐ _____

☐ _____

Results:

♥ _____ 💬 _____ 👤 _____ ✈ _____ 🔖 _____

Rating: ☆☆☆☆☆ **Time Posted:** _____ **Engagement Rate:** _____

Notes: _____

_____

Content Planner

Post Title: _____

Keywords: _____

Hashtags: _____

Content Details:

Notes:

_____

_____

_____

_____

_____

_____

_____

_____

_____

To Do List:

☐ Brainstorm Content

☐ Graphic Creation

☐ Affiliate & Sponsor Links

☐ Call to Action

☐ Grammar Check

☐ Link Check

☐ Post Scheduling

☐ Post Premiere

☐ _____

☐ _____

Results:

♥ _____   💬 _____   👤 _____   ◹ _____   🔖 _____

Rating: ☆☆☆☆☆   **Time Posted:** _____   **Engagement Rate:** _____

Notes: _____

Content Planner

Post Title: _____

Keywords: _____

Hashtags: _____

Content Details:

Notes:

_____

_____

_____

_____

_____

_____

_____

_____

_____

To Do List:

☐ Brainstorm Content

☐ Graphic Creation

☐ Affiliate & Sponsor Links

☐ Call to Action

☐ Grammar Check

☐ Link Check

☐ Post Scheduling

☐ Post Premiere

☐ _____

☐ _____

Results:

♥ _____   💬 _____   👤 _____   ◸ _____   🔖 _____

Rating: ☆☆☆☆☆   **Time Posted:** _____   **Engagement Rate:** _____

Notes: _____

Content Planner

Post Title: _____

Keywords: _____

Hashtags: _____

Content Details:

Notes:

_____

_____

_____

_____

_____

_____

_____

_____

_____

_____

To Do List:

- ☐ Brainstorm Content
- ☐ Graphic Creation
- ☐ Affiliate & Sponsor Links
- ☐ Call to Action
- ☐ Grammar Check
- ☐ Link Check
- ☐ Post Scheduling
- ☐ Post Premiere
- ☐ _____
- ☐ _____

Results:

♥ _____   💬 _____   👤 _____   ✈ _____   🔖 _____

Rating: ☆☆☆☆☆   **Time Posted:** _____   **Engagement Rate:** _____

Notes: _____

_____

Content Planner

Post Title: _____

Keywords: _____

Hashtags: _____

Content Details:

Notes:

_____

_____

_____

_____

_____

_____

_____

_____

To Do List:

- ☐ Brainstorm Content
- ☐ Graphic Creation
- ☐ Affiliate & Sponsor Links
- ☐ Call to Action
- ☐ Grammar Check
- ☐ Link Check
- ☐ Post Scheduling
- ☐ Post Premiere
- ☐ _____
- ☐ _____

Results:

♥ _____   💬 _____   👤 _____   ✈ _____   🔖 _____

Rating: ☆☆☆☆☆   **Time Posted:** _____   **Engagement Rate:** _____

Notes: _____

_____

Content Planner

Post Title: _____

Keywords: _____

Hashtags: _____

Content Details:

Notes:

_____

_____

_____

_____

_____

_____

_____

_____

_____

_____

To Do List:

☐ Brainstorm Content

☐ Graphic Creation

☐ Affiliate & Sponsor Links

☐ Call to Action

☐ Grammar Check

☐ Link Check

☐ Post Scheduling

☐ Post Premiere

☐ _____

☐ _____

Results:

♥ _____   💬 _____   👤 _____   ✈ _____   🔖 _____

Rating: ☆☆☆☆☆   **Time Posted:** _____   **Engagement Rate:** _____

Notes: _____

_____

Content Planner

Post Title: _____

Keywords: _____

Hashtags: _____

Content Details:

Notes:

_____

_____

_____

_____

_____

_____

_____

_____

_____

_____

To Do List:

☐ Brainstorm Content _____

☐ Graphic Creation _____

☐ Affiliate & Sponsor Links _____

☐ Call to Action _____

☐ Grammar Check _____

☐ Link Check _____

☐ Post Scheduling _____

☐ Post Premiere _____

☐ _____

☐ _____

Results:

♥ _____ 💬 _____ 👤 _____ ⏵ _____ 🔖 _____

Rating: ☆☆☆☆☆ **Time Posted:** _____ **Engagement Rate:** _____

Notes: _____

_____

Content Planner

Post Title: _____

Keywords: _____

Hashtags: _____

Content Details:

Notes:

_____

_____

_____

_____

_____

_____

_____

_____

_____

To Do List:

☐ Brainstorm Content

☐ Graphic Creation

☐ Affiliate & Sponsor Links

☐ Call to Action

☐ Grammar Check

☐ Link Check

☐ Post Scheduling

☐ Post Premiere

☐ _____

☐ _____

Results:

♥ _____   💬 _____   👤 _____   ◹ _____   🔖 _____

Rating: ☆☆☆☆☆   **Time Posted:** _____   **Engagement Rate:** _____

Notes: _____

Content Planner

Post Title: _____

Keywords: _____

Hashtags: _____

```
┌─────────────────────────────────────────────┐
│              Content Details:               │
│                                             │
│                                             │
│                                             │
│                                             │
│                                             │
│                                             │
│                                             │
│                                             │
│                                             │
└─────────────────────────────────────────────┘
```

Notes:

_____

_____

_____

_____

_____

_____

_____

_____

_____

_____

To Do List:

- ☐ Brainstorm Content
- ☐ Graphic Creation
- ☐ Affiliate & Sponsor Links
- ☐ Call to Action
- ☐ Grammar Check
- ☐ Link Check
- ☐ Post Scheduling
- ☐ Post Premiere
- ☐ _____
- ☐ _____

Results:

♥ _____   💬 _____   👤 _____   ✈ _____   🔖 _____

Rating: ☆☆☆☆☆   **Time Posted:** _____   **Engagement Rate:** _____

Notes: _____

_____